THE
BISON
OF
YELLOWSTONE
NATIONAL PARK

Margaret Mary Meagher
Research Biologist
National Park Service

National Park Service
Scientific Monograph Series
Number One
1973

Richard Nixon
President of the United States

Rogers C. B. Morton, Secretary
U.S. Department of the Interior

Ronald H. Walker, Director
National Park Service

As the Nation's principal conservation agency, the Department of
the Interior has basic responsibilities for water, fish, wildlife,
mineral, land, park, and recreational resources. Indian and
Territorial affairs are other major concerns of America's "Department of Natural Resources." The Department works to assure the
wisest choice in managing all our resources so each will make its
full contribution to a better United States—now and in the
future.

This publication is one in a series of research studies devoted to
special topics which have been explored in connection with the
various areas in the National Park System. It is printed at the
Government Printing Office and may be purchased from the
Superintendent of Documents, Government Printing Office,
Washington, D.C. 20402. Price $2.25. Stock No. 2405–00524

Library of Congress Catalog Card Number: 73-600221

Acknowledgments

THIS RESEARCH WAS UNDERTAKEN with the sponsorship of the National Park Service and the Museum of Vertebrate Zoology, University of California, Berkeley. The research report, accepted as a doctoral dissertation in 1970 by the University of California, is presented here with minor modifications.

The project, conducted over a span of 7 years while I was employed as a Park Naturalist by the National Park Service at Yellowstone National Park, would not have been possible without the assistance of many people. Among the National Park Service personnel who contributed, particular appreciation is due John Good, former Chief Park Naturalist, for encouragement and assistance in arranging work requirements to allow time for the study. Park Rangers Peter Thompson, Dale Nuss, and Gordon Boyd assisted with some of the field work. Biologist Glen Cole contributed ideas and suggestions. Aubrey Haines provided information on historical sources.

Dave Stradley, Gallatin Flying Service, made possible the quality of the aerial observation work. Kenneth Greer, Supervisor of the Montana State Fish and Game Department Laboratory, provided food habits analysis assistance. W. E. Booth, Montana State University, verified plant identifications. John Ricks, Livingston, Montana, facilitated autopsy work. Keith Hoofnagle did the maps and graphs.

Financial support was provided by the National Park Service and the Union Foundation Wildlife Fund, administered by the University of California. The Yellowstone Library and Museum Association contributed to the reproduction of dissertation copies.

To these people and organizations, and the many other individuals who provided information, encouragement, and assistance—my thanks.

July 1972   MARGARET MARY MEAGHER

Summary

OBJECTIVES OF THIS STUDY were to provide basic data on the life history, habits, and ecology of bison in Yellowstone National Park.

The original population of bison in historic times consisted of mountain bison, *Bison bison athabascae*. In spite of poaching to near-extermination by about 1901, a remnant of the subspecies survived and increased. Interbreeding with a population of plains bison, *B. b. bison*, introduced in 1902, began by the 1920s. The present bison population consists of hybrid descendants of the two subspecies.

The present wintering distribution within the park approximates that of the historic population, occurring in the three subunits of Lamar, Pelican, and Mary Mountain, none of which are geographically isolated from the others. The present summering population approximates the historic distribution only in the Upper Lamar-Mirror Plateau and Hayden Valley areas. A large west-side and a large northern summering population are lacking. Present (1968) numbers are half or less than those of probable historic numbers.

Examination of 71 females killed for population reduction purposes indicated that sexual maturity was not reached by most until 4 years of age, later than recorded some years ago. The observed pregnancy rate of 52% for females 2.5 years and older was also less than formerly recorded in Yellowstone. Brucellosis was not a factor which affected reproduction. Records and observations suggested that both calving season (in May on the winter ranges) and the breeding season (in late July to early August on the summer ranges) were shorter than formerly. The observed changes may reflect the shift from a semiranched population to a wild one.

Records from live-trapping operations in 1964-66 provided sex and age structure information. The records suggested that female survival was favored during the calf year, but that male survival was favored the next 3 years of life, after which differential survival could not be distinguished from the records. Adult bulls outnumbered adult cows, but this could be attributed to earlier reductions.

Age classes of the wintering population in the Mary Mountain area in 1964-65 were: calves, 16%; yearlings, 11%; 2.5-year-olds, 6%; 3.5-year-olds, 5%; and adults, 62%. These may change somewhat after a period with no reductions.

Observed spring calf percentages of mixed herd numbers for 3 of 5 years were 19-20%. Percentages of total population were approximately 11%. These percentages may also change if reductions are not made.

Significant mortality of calves at birth or just before or after was suggested by limited data. Thereafter, little mortality occurred during the first year. Nearly half the calves which survived into their first winter died before 2.5 years of age. Recruitment into the population occurred with survival to 3 years of age.

Population trends suggested that increases in the population were often very slow. Reductions by man apparently were not the sole factor which caused population decreases nor retarded increases. Parasites, diseases, predation, and emigration were not important. Environmental factors culminating in usual and more-than-usual winter mortality appeared important.

Herd groups followed definite patterns of seasonal movement. Spring migrations to summer ranges, occurring by the second week of June, appeared to be influenced by weather patterns and temperatures rather than snow melt or vegetation changes. Temporary fall movements occurred in conjunction with fall storms at higher elevations; final movements to winter ranges occurred by mid-November. Bull movements were somewhat more irregular.

Movements and distribution on summer range areas appeared more influenced by the presence of biting flies than by possible factors of breeding activity and vegetation changes. A species of *Symphoromyia* of the Rhagionidae was implicated.

Mixing and interchange between population subunits resulted in designation of three herds according to their use of winter range areas. These three subunits formed two breeding populations in summer. Little contact occurred between members of these two populations at any time.

The limited neckband information on marked adult cows suggested that they have an affinity for a given winter range regardless of summer movements. Temporary shifts of population segments from one winter range to another have occurred. Thus, although no population segment is isolated from another, the three exist as fairly separate entities in terms of winter range. This may explain the lack of population emigration to and reestablishment on unoccupied ranges either within or outside the park since historic times.

Analysis of 22 rumen samples showed that sedge was the most important forage item. Sedge, rush, and grasses provided 96% of the diet volume throughout the year. Forage availability did not appear to be a population-limiting factor under most conditions.

Population numbers in Pelican over a span of many years suggested that the levels were regulated by environmental influences which resulted in low reproduction and low increment rates. Larger increases in numbers during favorable periods have been offset periodically by heavy mortality during more severe winters. The minimum population level in this area may be governed by the presence of scattered thermal areas used in winter stress periods. A combination of factors such as extensive sedge bottoms together with some sagebrush-grassland uplands, open streams, and thermal areas may allow habitation over time by mixed herd groups of bison in this wintering valley.

Contents

Chapter 9

SUGGESTED MECHANISMS
    OF POPULATION REGULATION

APPENDICES

Figures

Tables

1

Introduction

THE BISON OF YELLOWSTONE NA-
TIONAL PARK are unique among
bison herds in the United States,
being descendants, in part, of the
only continuously wild herd in this
country. They are today a hybrid
herd, being a mixture of the plains
bison (*Bison bison bison* Lin-
naeus), introduced into Yellowstone National Park in 1902, and
mountain or wood bison (*Bison
bison athabascae* Rhoads), which
originally inhabited the Yellowstone and surrounding country.
They are a wild population, unre-
stricted by either internal or
boundary fences, and subject to
minimal interference by man.

Although members of a species
which nearly became extinct, and a
species of great historical interest,
Yellowstone's bison have not been
objects of extensive research.
McHugh (1958) studied behavior
of bison in Yellowstone. Rush
(1932a), Tunnicliff and Marsh
(1935), and Locker (1953) pub-
lished information on parasites
and disease. Cahalane (1944)
summarized the history of the introduced herd and management
practices as of that date.

The present study was begun in
1963 to provide basic data on the
life history, habits, and ecology of
bison in the park. This study report, based on extensive field work
and supplemented by an intensive
search for historical information,
provides a basis for management
and for evaluation of the importance of this particular bison population. As a source of interpretive
information for the many people
who visit the park, the report may
make the bison less of a myth, but
a far more interesting reality.

Methods

Information on numbers, composition of groups, distribution,
and habits was obtained by using
fixed-wing aircraft and helicopter
flights, horse and ski travel, and
limited vehicle use. No set pattern
of route and interval was established; work was scheduled according to season, general animal
location, and distances involved.
Time of day was generally not a
factor. A monocular and a varia-
ble-power spotting scope were
used for observation.

Age and sex information was
compiled at herd-reduction opera-

1

tions at Lamar in the northeast quarter (Crystal trap) and on the Firehole River nearly 35 miles southwest of Lamar (Nez Perce trap) during the winters of 1964-65 and 1965-66. Reductions have been held in the park at intervals since 1932, primarily to keep the bison population at numbers suggested by range condition reports and surveys (Rush 1932b; Grimm 1939; Kittams 1947-58, 1949; Soil Conservation Service 1963, 1964). For reductions after 1960, animals have usually been driven into the two above-mentioned large live traps by coordinated herding efforts of two helicopters. Squeeze chutes permitted handling of most individuals, after which the bison were released or were trucked to a local slaughterhouse. Animals were selected for slaughter on the basis of brucellosis infection. Uninfected animals were also taken to fill removal quotas. All animals were permanently metal eartagged during brucellosis testing, and marked with temporary backtags, which were visible even from an airplane. Most were aged by Department of Agriculture veterinarians and weighed.

During both winters, some released animals were marked with color-coded neckbands for area and individual recognition, and for the year of banding. Animals—preferably females, yearlings and older—were chosen a few at a time on different trap days to distribute marked animals among released groups as much as possible. Forty-four individuals (30 of them females) were neckbanded, half at each trap. Seventeen females and two males were young adults and older. Half of the neckbands were lost during the first year. More males than females lost neckbands. Attempts to neckband animals through use of field immobilization techniques were not satisfactory.

During slaughter operations, approximately 47% of the animals removed from the park were examined for pregnancy, abnormalities, and evidence of injury or disease other than brucellosis. Reproductive tracts could not be examined, nor fetal sex ratios determined because approximately half of removed animals had brucellosis or were suspect. Department of Agriculture veterinarians advised against examination of reproductive organs, where the *Brucella* organism most often localizes, to avoid contamination of slaughterhouse premises and exposure of personnel to the disease. Lower jaws were collected for age verification using the techniques of Fuller (1959).

Food-habit information came from analysis of 22 rumen samples collected from animals shot in the park at all seasons and in various locations. Percent composition of samples was determined by volume after separation and identification of materials. The analyses were supplemented by general field observations of animal feeding behavior.

2
The Study Area

THE STUDY AREA INCLUDED all parts of Yellowstone National Park regularly used by the bison population, or frequented by them in the past 20-25 years (Fig. 1). The occupied bison range covers nearly half of Yellowstone's 3472 square miles, extending diagonally across the park from the northeast quarter to the southwest quarter. Some phases of study effort were emphasized in the northeast quarter. Lands outside the boundaries are not used to any extent by the park bison, and hence were not part of the study area, but they are discussed where pertinent to historical populations.

Physiography

Much of the park is plateau-like, varying in elevation from about 7000 to 8000 feet, and cut by large and small stream valleys (Fig. 2). Mountains project above the general level on all sides, but are less extensive in the interior. The Continental Divide traverses the park from west to southeast, generally unmarked by abrupt changes in terrain. Most of the study area lies east of the divide, and is drained by the headwaters of the Madison and Yellowstone rivers. Tributaries of the Snake River drain the southwestern corner.

Park geology is discussed by Hague (1899), whose work was followed by numerous topical studies. U.S. Geological Survey personnel are now completing a comprehensive research program which will add much to present knowledge of the complex geologic history of Yellowstone. Extensive volcanism, of which the widely distributed thermal activity is a remnant stage, has shaped many of the physiographic features. Effects of glaciers, which may have persisted as recently as 8000 years ago, are evident throughout the park.

The study area was subdivided into nine regions. From northeast to southwest these are: Lamar, Upper Lamar, Mirror Plateau, Pelican, Hayden Valley, Firehole, Madison Plateau, Pitchstone Plateau, and Bechler (Fig. 1). The Lamar (Fig. 3), at approximately

3

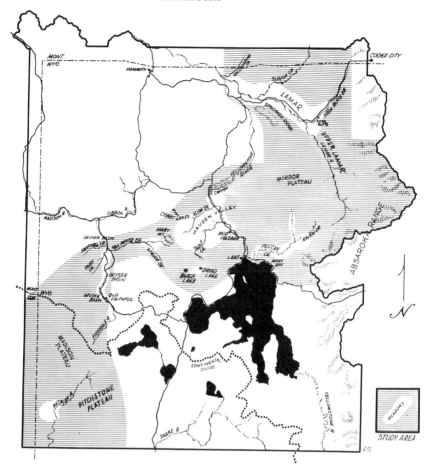

Fig. 1.   Map of Yellowstone National Park showing study area.

6400 feet, includes lower Hellroaring and Slough creeks, the main Lamar River Valley below Soda Butte Creek, the north-facing lower slopes of Specimen Ridge, and the Soda Butte area. The Upper Lamar refers to the Lamar River above Soda Butte Creek, together with the ridges and tributaries rising eastward to the Absaroka Mountains, at more than 10,000 feet Fig. 4). The Mirror Plateau, including much of Specimen Ridge, lies between the Lamar

Fig. 2. Aerial view of a part of the forested plateau, located centrally.

River to the north and east, the Yellowstone River to the west, and Pelican Valley to the south. Pelican Valley (Fig. 5), at 7800 feet, refers to the main valley from the lowest portions of Raven Creek to the mouth of Pelican Creek and includes Mary Bay on Yellowstone Lake. Hayden Valley, elevation 7700 feet, is centrally located in the park (Fig. 6). It extends from the Grand Canyon of the Yellowstone south to the Mud Volcano, west to Mary Mountain, and includes Beach and Dryad lakes to the south and Cygnet Lakes to the north. The Firehole, at 7200 feet,

refers to all three major geyser basins along that river, together with Nez Perce, Spruce, Sentinel, and Fairy creeks (Fig. 7). West of the Firehole, the Madison Plateau rises gradually to the Continental Divide and extends to the Bechler Meadows. The Pitchstone Plateau (Fig. 8) lies southeast of the Madison Plateau. The Bechler Meadows, at 6400 feet, are comparable to the Lamar in elevation.

Soils vary greatly. Generally, there are deep silts in the bottoms of the big valleys. Morainal materials are especially prominent in Lamar. Lake deposits of clays and

Fig. 3. Springtime view west across part of the bison winter use area of the lower Lamar Valley.

Fig. 4. The upper Lamar drainage with the edge of the Mirror Plateau to the right, a
part of the Absaroka Mountains in the background.

Fig. 5. Bison on the Pelican Valley winter range.

Fig. 6. A part of the Hayden Valley winter range with Alum Creek in the foreground.

Fig. 7. The Lower Geyser Basin area of the Firehole winter range in early spring.

sands are found in Pelican and Hayden valleys. Higher areas commonly have shallow, poorly developed soils derived from volcanic parent material interspersed with alluvial sites.

Climate

Throughout the area winters are long and cold, with short cool summers. The U.S. Department of Commerce Weather Bureau (1930-59) summary for Yellowstone National Park indicated for the headquarters' station at Mammoth, near the north boundary, a mean annual temperature of 39.8°F. January, the coldest month, averaged 18.0°F; July, with a mean of 62.8°F, was the warmest. Temperatures at this station average about 5°F higher than those for most of the park.

The same summary indicated that average annual precipitation in the study area varied from 13.73 inches at Lamar to 38.26 inches at Bechler. Near Pelican, the annual average was 19.00 inches. Most precipitation occurred as snow. For most of the park, between the 7000- and 8500-foot levels, the average snowfall was about 150 inches, with Lamar averaging 85-95 inches, and Lake, near Pelican, averaging 146 inches. For a 50-year period at Lake, a range in snowfall of 81-270 inches is recorded. Actual depth on the ground at Lake, as recorded by snow survey measurements (U.S. Department of Agriculture—Soil Conservation Service, 1919-67), averaged about 19 inches for 1 January and about 35 inches by 1 April. Lamar would usually have somewhat less; Bechler, somewhat more. Crusting conditions, for which no record is available, varied considerably.

Seasons of the year vary with location and altitude. Warm sites near thermal activity are snow-free earlier and have a longer growing season than surrounding areas. Winter extended from mid-November to mid-April in all areas of the study. Spring began in mid-April in Lamar, in mid-May in the higher valleys, and on 1 July at the highest elevations. Summer began 1 July in the valleys, late July in the mountains. Killing frosts are usual in most locations before the end of August, so fall extended from 1 September to mid-November in all areas. At higher elevations, snow depth was often considerable by early November.

Vegetation

Vegetation types were not mapped for purposes of this study. Figure 1 indicates the extent of the larger meadows within the forested parts of the study area. More detail is apparent in Figs. 30 and 31, which show subunits of the study area. Major species of plants, according to site, are

Fig. 8. Summer range on the western part of the Pitchstone Plateau.

listed in Table 1. General descriptions of park vegetation are
provided by Bailey (1930), Bailey
and Bailey (1949), and McDougall
and Baggley (1956). Common and
scientific names used are listed in
Appendix I. These follow Booth
(1950) or Booth and Wright
(1959).

The large, open valleys of Lamar, Pelican, Hayden, and Firehole have dense sedge growth
bordering the streams and extending across the flat bottoms. The
slightly higher slopes and levels
support bunchgrasses, forbs, and
sagebrush, with scattered marshy
swale areas. Shrubs, except sagebrush, are of limited extent generally in these valleys. In Lamar, wil-
low was grubbed out in some
places to increase the area of pasture and hay land during early
Buffalo Ranch operations. Extensive grassland and sagebrush areas
on high slopes and ridges are particularly common in the northeast
quarter, although patches of more
lush herbaceous vegetation are
frequent.

Much of the study area is forested, predominantly by lodgepole
pine, which varies from dense,
even-age growth with little under-
story to open stands with considerable sedge and grass. Dense shrub-
by undergrowth is usually not extensive. Down timber is common.
At higher elevations, Engelmann
spruce and alpine fir replace the
lodgepole. Whitebark pine is
found in some locations. Meadows

are scattered throughout the forest on moist sites along streams
and around ponds, and appear as
small openings in drier locations.
Particularly on the Mirror Plateau,
boggy side hills with dense sedge
growth are numerous.

On the upper plateau levels and
mountain slopes, subalpine meadows are found. Above these, at the
highest elevations, alpine vegetation occurs to a limited extent.

History

Yellowstone National Park was
established in 1872, before the
surrounding area became the
states of Idaho, Montana, and
Wyoming. Boundary changes,
made twice, added small areas to
the original rectangle and altered
the east boundary in 1929 to con-
form for most of its length to the
drainage divide formed by the
Absaroka Mountains. Most of the
land adjacent to the boundary is
administered by the U.S. Forest
Service.

Haines (1963) summarizes the
history of man's occupation of the
Yellowstone Plateau. Prehistoric
hunters and gatherers used the
area extensively. Members of several tribes of modern Indians were
primarily summer hunters, although a few sheep-eaters lived a
marginal existence throughout the
year. Hostile Indians did not travel
the park after the Bannock War of
1878, but hunting parties from

TABLE 1. *Vegetation of the study area.*

Vegetation type	General distribution	Characteristic vegetation	Associated plants
Marsh	Alluvial soils along watercourses, swale areas	Tufted Hairgrass-Sedge Sedge-Bluegrass	Rush Shrubby Cinquefoil
Sagebrush-Grassland	Glacial outwash areas, alluvial fans, lacustrine deposits	Big Sagebrush	Wheatgrass Idaho Fescue Balsamroot Lupine Eriogonum Dryland Sedges
Upland Forest	Various substrates and exposures up to 10,000 ft.	Lodgepole Pine Engelmann Spruce-Subalpine Fir Whitebark Pine	Dwarf Huckleberry Arnica Lupine Pinegrass
Forest Park	Alluvial soils along watercourses, old ponds, small openings on drier slopes	Sedge-Tufted Hairgrass Idaho Fescue-Wheatgrass Mountain Brome-Slender Wheatgrass	Rush Dandelion Lupine Cinquefoil Bluegrass
Herbland	Fine-textured residual soils of mountain slopes from about 8000 to 9500 ft.	Mountain Brome-Slender Wheatgrass	Lupine Cinquefoil Geranium
Subalpine Meadow	Mountain slopes and ridgetops, mainly above 8500 ft.	Tufted Hairgrass-Sedge	Rush Bluegrass Wild Barley Bluegrass Needlegrass Rush

reservations were known at the park fringes as late as 1893 (Hough 1894). Although few left written accounts, trappers, beginning with John Colter in 1807, visited the area many times before the end of the fur trade in 1840. Miners and explorers followed.

The park was not subject to settlement, and there were few people for some years after its establishment. With the exception of a few early squatters, developments were for administrative use or concessioner operation. In conjunction with these, horses and cattle were grazed in some places, and wild hay was cut. Disturbance was generally minimal except in the Lamar area. Skinner and Alcorn (1942-51) summarize the Buffalo Ranch-Lamar Ranger Station operations of Lamar and Slough Creek valleys from 1907 through 1951. Seeding and irrigation practices were part of the haying program, as well as construction of buildings, fences, and other necessities of a ranch.

During the early years of the park, wildlife had little protection. The Act establishing Yellowstone National Park provided only that wildlife should not be "wantonly destroyed" nor subject to "capture and destruction for the purposes of merchandise or profit." Until 1887 official regulations permitted hunting while traveling in the park. Legal means for enforcing regulations were lacking, although the Army troops stationed in the park after 1886 did what they could. Attempts at protection had limited effect until passage of the Lacey Act in 1894 provided legal machinery and jurisdictional authority for dealing with violators. Outside the park, ineffective laws contributed to poaching within the boundaries.

Not until 1901 did the Superintendent of the park believe the laws of all three surrounding states were such that the wild bison left in Yellowstone might be effectively protected, but their numbers were so few that survival seemed doubtful. Intensive management of an introduced herd began in 1902 to ensure survival of some bison in Yellowstone. For a time the animals lived in semidomestication, and were fed hay and tended almost like a herd of cattle. Management policy gradually changed to one of minimal interference by man, which continues in spite of the impact of steadily increasing numbers of tourists. The present (1970) bison population is completely wild and unfettered by fencing or artificial management.

3
The Bison Population

The Historic Population

THE GENUS *Bison* PROBABLY IN- VADED North America during the later part of the early Pleistocene. The bison occupying the continent in historic times were descendants of a second migration of *Bison* from Eurasia, which crossed the Bering Straits at the start of the late Pleistocene according to Skinner and Kaisen (1947). Of the invading species, only one persisted to give rise to *B. occidentalis*, the ancestor of *B. bison*, the modern form. Two subspecies, *B. b. bison* and *B. b. athabascae*, are recognized by cranial evidence, although historical accounts suggest there may have been others (Roe 1951). The form *athabascae* is apparently the more primitive of the two subspecies (Skinner and Kaisen 1947).

Just when bison first reached the Yellowstone plateau is not known, but modern bison inhabited the area before historic times, perhaps before the most recent period of intermountain glaciation. Bone fragments from bulls, cows, and calves (*B. bison*) were found near the edge of a glacier northeast of

Yellowstone National Park (Pattie and Verbeek 1967). In 1964 a fossil cranium (*B. b. athabascae*) was found embedded in a natural oil seep on the Mirror Plateau in the park.

The Yellowstone bison of historic times were a remnant of a once much more extensive bison population, known to trappers and Indians, which inhabited the mountain ranges and the intermountain valleys of the Rockies and extended on west into Washington and Oregon. Most of these bison were gone by the 1840s (Aubrey Haines 1968 pers. comm.). According to the distribution map of Skinner and Kaisen (1947), these were mountain bison. Considerable numbers of bison once lived close to the park. Many skulls have been found in the Red Rock Lakes area, approximately 35 miles west of Yellowstone (Owen Vivion 1968 pers. comm.) Frank Childs, former Yellowstone ranger who worked on Red Rocks land acquisition matters during the mid-1930s, heard that 300 bison died there during a bad winter many

13

years earlier (1965 pers. comm.). Many skulls have also been taken from the Mud Lake area of Idaho, approximately 55 miles southwest of Yellowstone (Richard Wilson 1968 pers. comm.). Osborne Russell, writing in 1835, mentions the large numbers of buffalo (bison) seen in both the Red Rock and Mud Lake areas (Haines 1955). Doane (1876) comments that "buffalo skulls are strewn by thousands —" in the Yellowstone valley about 40 miles north of the park. Accounts of wild bison adjacent to and within the park, dating from 1860 through 1902 (Appendix II), leave no doubt that substantial numbers of bison inhabited the Yellowstone Plateau at all seasons, and long before the killing of the northern herd of Great Plains bison in the early 1880s.

A misconception of some writers —that Yellowstone's bison of historic times were displaced survivors from the Great Plains slaughter—probably stems from: (1) the lack of recognition of two subspecies of *Bison bison*; and (2) the impression that early explorers found little "game" in the Rocky Mountains. Three factors contribute to the idea that bison were sparse in the mountains. Compared to the abundance of certain large mammals on the plains, the mountains probably seemed almost uninhabited. Secondly, travel routes followed river valleys and drainages, crossing small areas of high summer range at few loca-

tions, often at a season when biting insects may have driven the game from the lower elevations of passes to adjacent higher slopes and ridges. Finally, the few early travelers who wrote of their journeys, including official government parties, often commented only on wildlife which was actually sought out or shot for food.

Mountain Bison

The existence of mountain bison, different in appearance and behavior from the plains type and gone from much of their range by the 1840s, has generally been little known. Christman (1971) reviews historical evidence for the subspecies, their distribution to the west of the plains type, and reasons for their early disappearance. He believes the Indians' acquisition of the horse was the factor underlying the extermination of mountain bison from extensive areas of original range, particularly in Washington, Oregon, and Idaho.

Many early references to Yellowstone bison use the term "wood" or more commonly "mountain" bison or buffalo (Fig. 9); some of the characteristics of the race were recognized by a number of early travelers and observers. Historical accounts generally agree that, compared with the plains bison, these mountain animals were more hardy, fleet, and wary, and had darker, finer, curl-

Fig. 9. Cows and calves photographed in a remote part of Hayden Valley sometime before 1894. These bison were frequently called mountain bison by early observers. Photo by John Folsom, a winterkeeper at Canyon.

ier hair. Sex and age differences among animals seen may account for discrepancies in description of size. The geologist Arnold Hague (1893) provides the following:

> The Park buffalo may all be classed under the head of mountain buffalo and even in this elevated region they live for the greater part of the year in the timber. . . .most unusual, save in midwinter, to find them in open valley or on the treeless mountain slope. They haunt the most inaccessible and out-of-the-way places, . . . living in open glades and pastures, the oases of the dense forest, . . . the rapidity of their disappearance on being alarmed. It is surprising how few buffalo have been seen in midsummer, even by those most familiar with their haunts and habits. They wander about in small bands. . . .

Blackmore (1872) was informed that the mountain buffalo congregated usually in bands of 5-30, rarely more. Other observers agree that the bands were small, and the animals quite wary. Superintendent Norris described them as "most keen of scent and difficult of approach of all mountain animals" (Superintendent of the Yellowstone National Park 1880).

Altitudinal migrations were another characteristic of mountain bison (Christman 1971). Historical accounts from Yellowstone also suggest this habit. Superintendent Norris, in his annual report of 1880, describes summer and winter distributions of bison in the park, stating clearly:

> . . .summer in the valleys of the Crevice, Hellroaring, and Slough Creeks, and the mountain spurs between them, descending with the increasing snows, to winter . . .East Fork [Lamar]. . .and as the snows melt . . .returning to their old haunts.

The historical accounts of dates and locations of bison (Appendix II) collectively also show a repetitive pattern of seasonal bison distribution which reflects altitudinal movements.

Historical accounts recognizing a mountain buffalo are supported by limited cranial evidence. Skinner and Kaisen (1947) show an overlap in general distribution between mountain and plains bison along the east slopes of the Rockies, including Yellowstone, but state that ranges for historic times must be based on early accounts plus occasional bones or crania. Seven skulls from Yellowstone's original wild herd were picked up on the ground along the Gardner River and at Mammoth in 1902. All had weathered surfaces. These were considered as most likely representing *athabascae*. The 1964 skull (Fig. 10) found

Fig. 10. Skulls of *Bison bison athabascae* (left) and *B. b. bison* from the Mirror Plateau, Yellowstone National Park. Photo by David Love, U.S. Geological Survey.

on the Mirror Plateau was identified by Skinner (1965) as "an exceptionally long horned, apparently young Mountain bison = *B. (B.)b. athabascae . . . .*" No Yellowstone skulls which predate the 1902 introduction have been identified as plains type.

Numbers and Distribution through 1902

Numbers and distributions from the historical accounts of Appendix II are shown in Table 2. Norris (Superintendent of the Yellowstone National Park 1880) estimated a total of 600, dividing the population into three herds according to area. By this date, poaching had certainly begun inside the park, along with increasing pressure on an ever-shrinking mountain bison population outside. Numbers in a given area fluctuated then as now. After consideration of all the listed reports of numbers and distribution, the historical population, ranging in part beyond the park boundaries, is estimated to have been perhaps 1000 animals. This seems reasonable when bison habits and behavior and difficulties of making counts are all considered. Subestimates by area and season are at the bottom of Table 2. They are made to provide a reference point and must be considered educated guesses.

Table 2 also shows the decline of the population to an actual count of 23 in 1902. Again—considering habits, behavior, and census difficulties—the population probably was higher; perhaps 40-50 mountain bison survived. The near-extinction in about 25 years was the result, initially, of sport and table hunting on both sides of the park boundary, plus market hunting, particularly in the Lamar, by both the park hotel construction crews and the Cooke City miners. The capture of calves by local ranchers interested in starting private herds was probably most prevalent in Lamar and the west-side wintering areas. Finally, as bison everywhere verged on extinction, the price paid for heads, plus the minor penalties if caught, attracted poachers who killed all ages and both sexes in the wintering areas. Known losses as listed do not reflect the extent of the kill. Although the Howell poaching case resulted in passage of the Lacey Act in 1894, the population declined further as poaching, primarily from the west side, continued. Natural losses, coupled with scattering of the few remaining animals, left a minimal breeding population in the most remote places of the Pelican-Mirror-Upper Lamar country.

The distribution, to the extent known, of the original population was similar to the present distribution, but larger numbers used certain areas more extensively and

TABLE 2. *Summary, native bison information, 1860-1915.*

Year	West of Firehole[a]	Firehole	Hayden Valley	Pelican Valley	Mirror- Upper Lamar	Lamar Valley	North of Lamar	Other	Location not stated	Known losses	Official estimate (total)
1860	one band[b]										
1863	many trails										
186–							herd				
1870		numerous sign			some		thousands				
1871		tracks									
1872					herd	groups				7 calves captured	
1875									abundant	scores hunted	
1877				←——— 300-400 ———→							
1878	signs										
1880	300			←——— 100 ———→		←— 200 —→					
1881	small band		small band			some					
1883	small band					presumed			400; one band	market hunting	600

Year	Observations	Counts / sign	Population estimate	Hunting
1884		180	200	7 tourist hunting
1885	90 estim.	40	200-300	market hunting / poaching / 20 tourist hunting
1886				decrease in market hunting
1887	much scattered	9-10 54 40-80 20-30	100	
1888		200 — 100	increasing	
1889		some abundant fresh sign		
1890				small band, larger groups—winter
1891	60 + 12-15 calves, sing. & other small groups	30 + calves	increasing 200-400	poaching

TABLE 2. (continued) *Summary, native bison information, 1860-1915.*

Year	West of Firehole[a]	Firehole	Hayden Valley	Pelican Valley	Mirror-Upper Lamar	Lamar Valley	North of Lamar	Other	Location not stated	Known losses	Official estimate (total)
1892			300			some				poaching implied 2 calves captured	400; 20% calves
1893		50-60 inc. 13 calves							seen often	12 poached	400
1894			103	6 + 7					a few inc. calves	24 45-50	200 150
1895	100 (rumor)		30						3 + 4 + 10	3 calves west side poaching	200
1896	presumed			presumed					3 + 12 + 3 sign 9	10 est. west side poaching	25-50
1897	sign 20		sign 5	sign 2							24-50
1898	1 + 5	sign 3; sign 2; sign 4; 1 + 2	sign 5-6	1 + 5 sign 21	some						50
1899			5 + 1	20	2 + 4 + 3 + 15			1-Thorofare 2-Snake R.		1 calf	50 +

Year						
1900	39	poaching implied	29			
1901	25					
1902	25			22		1
1903		2 ♂ calves captured for introduced herd			16 adults 3 calves 19 adults—winter	
1904		1 ♀ calf captured for introduced herd, 4 Ad. 1 Yrlg.		12 (summer)	11 (5 ♀ 6 ♂)	2
1905	30			30		
1907 sign 6	25			sign 15		4
1908	increasing			20 maximum	2 adults ♂	
1909 sign		1 ♂ calf captured for introduced herd		spring, summer	23 + sign	
1910				5 + sign	29 max.	

TABLE 2. (continued) *Summary, native bison information, 1860-1915.*

Year	West of Firehole [a]	Firehole	Hayden Valley	Pelican Valley	Mirror-Upper Lamar	Lamar Valley	North of Lamar	Other	Location not stated	Known losses	Official estimate (total)
1911			8	27 inc. 2 calves	sign 1						
1912	1 ♂				48 including 10 calves						49 thriving
1913				53							increasing
1914									considerable numbers		increasing
1915				31 (5 ♂, 6 yrlg., 4 calves inc.)							
Estimate of Historic Population, Winter		some	300								
Estimate of Historic Population, Summer 300			200		300-400	200-300	400				

[a] Primarily Madison-Pitchstone Plateaus.
[b] Just outside the West boundary.

ranged beyond the park boundaries part of the time. Figure 11 shows the probable general distribution and population movements of mixed herd groups. The term "mixed group," as in Fuller (1960), is used here also for groups which usually contain some mature bulls as well as cows and young. Four areas of summer range and five of winter range are indicated. In two locations the population probably moved across present boundary lines in numbers.

From northeast to southwest, the four areas of historic summer range were: north of Lamar, Upper Lamar-Mirror Plateau, Hayden Valley, and Madison-Pitchstone plateaus. Large numbers of bison apparently ranged at least three of the four areas. North of Lamar, the summering herds of the northern part of the Absaroka Range split south to the Lamar Valley and north beyond the park to other valleys to winter. On the west side, the greater part of the summering herds of the Madison-Pitchstone plateaus probably moved southwest beyond the park toward the east end of the Snake River plains (Mud Lake area) as Norris presumed (Superintendent of the Yellowstone National Park 1880). Historically, as now, the Upper Lamar-Mirror Plateau was used extensively. The importance of Hayden Valley as historic summer range is less clear. Some of the bison which wintered in Hayden Valley apparently moved west to

the Madison Plateau in summer. People, traveling perhaps when the bands were south of the main valley in the forested areas, may rarely have seen a group. Hague's (1893) reference to the borders of Elephant Back (south of Hayden Valley) as summer range suggests that bison did regularly summer in the area. Perhaps it was the least important summer range.

Large numbers of bison regularly wintered in Lamar, Pelican, and Hayden valleys (Fig. 12). The Firehole seems to have been less important. Snow conditions common in the Bechler Meadows make it unlikely that large numbers habitually wintered there, but certainly small groups must have since calves were captured there in early spring (Murri 1968).

Historical reports do not indicate groups along the Madison and Gallatin rivers to the northwest, within the park, but Raynolds (1867), while crossing from Henry's Lake to the Madison River, just west of the park, in 1860 reported bison "among the hills, . . ." Small groups of bison, also unreported, may have used the large grasslands just north of the Madison River (south of Cougar Creek) as they did in the 1950s.

Knowledge of travel routes used by people during the early days of the park, which probably followed main game trails, suggests relative game population numbers, locations, and movements (Fig. 11).

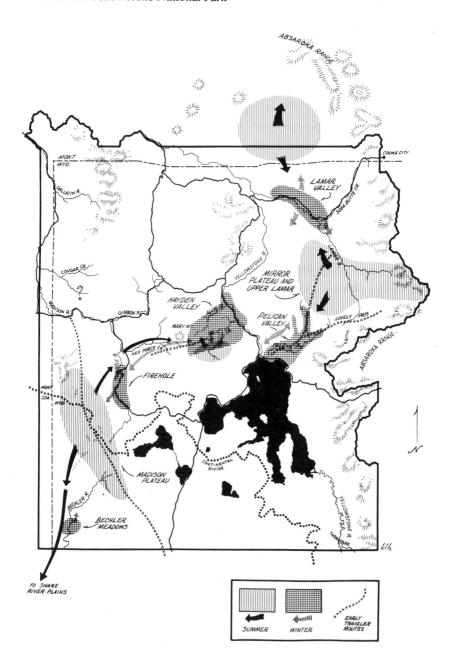

Fig. 11. Map of general distribution and movements of bison mixed herd groups in historic times.

Fig. 12. Bison wintering in Hayden Valley prior to 1894. Photo probably by John Folsom, early Canyon winterkeeper.

Hague (1893) mentions the lack of buffalo trails, but he was comparing Yellowstone to the plains. Definite buffalo trails did exist (DeLacy 1876). Norris' (Superintendent of the Yellowstone National Park 1880) map shows a trail northeast across the Mirror Plateau which follows the route of present buffalo trails. The usual Pelican-Upper Lamar route (in part an elk trail) once crossed Lovely Pass between Raven and Mist creeks (Superintendent of the Yellowstone National Park 1897). Movement of bison across the Mary Mountain route between Hayden Valley and the Firehole, commonly used by people prior to construction of a road along Yellowstone Lake, was implied by earlier writers, and stated as fact by Hough in 1894. Routes in use by patrols on the Madison Plateau further support early reports of size and distribution of a large west-side summering population which may have extended north across the Madison River.

Finally, scattered individuals, probably bulls, must occasionally, then as now, have been found in peripheral areas. Although early reports of live bison are lacking, some animals must surely have inhabited places in the northwest quarter of the park outside the known or presumed distribution of herd groups. In the southeast, Holt (1899) recorded a buffalo in the Thorofare area. A skull from Two Ocean Pass (Fryxell 1926) just south of the boundary, found before 1925, presumably belonged to another such individual.

The Present Population

Origins

As stated previously, the Yellowstone bison of the present derive from two subspecies: plains bison from Montana (Pablo-Allard herd) and Texas (Goodnight herd), introduced in 1902, and a remnant of the original wild population of mountain bison. Skinner and Alcorn (1942-51) summarize the introduction, numbers, and subsequent management practices pertaining to the introduced herd at the Buffalo Ranch in Lamar. Population numbers are from that source and other official reports. Skinner also provides a resumé of official information concerning the wild bison, but does not attempt to evaluate the question of their survival. Information scattered in the diaries, reports, and correspondence of park personnel (Yellowstone National Park Archives) provides the basis for the following.

Before 1915, introduced bison of plains stock could not have escaped to form a wild group. The introduced herd was in a small fenced pasture at Mammoth from 1902 until moved to the Buffalo Ranch at Lamar in 1907. From 1907 until at least 1915, these animals were closely day-herded, and apparently put in a fenced pasture at night. Although one plains bull from the fenced herd was turned out in 1903, and one or two stray bulls were mentioned later in scout reports, these apparently never joined the wild bison. Twenty bulls from the Buffalo Ranch were driven 14 miles up the Lamar River in 1914; these all returned.

Members of two other small groups of semidomestic bison, those of the Yellowstone Lake Boat Co. and some from Henry's Lake west of the park, never mixed with the wild herd (Appendix III).

In spite of very low numbers and a pessimistic outlook, the original wild herd did persist, and gradually increased once protection from poaching was assured. The critical survival period extended from 1902 until about 1920; thereafter, groups of bison which did not frequent the Buffalo Ranch were more common. These probably contained escapees from the introduced herd as well as native animals. Table 2, from sources listed in Appendix III, shows dates, locations, and numbers for the wild herd from 1903-15. Later official estimates of wild herd numbers are not used, since there was some possibility of wild and introduced animals intermingling after 1915. The table shows clearly the presence of a remnant wild herd in Pelican Valley in winter, and on the Mirror Plateau in summer, as well as a few individuals elsewhere. There was a steady increase, indicated both by calves and by total bison seen. The known population more than doubled between 1903 and 1912.

An actual count was difficult, as Nowlin (1912) of the Biological Survey found: "I have never seen buffaloes on the range so wary and difficult to locate as the wild ones in the Yellowstone Park."

Official population estimates of the time did not allow for more animals than were actually seen; they were undoubtedly conservative. By 1912, as Nowlin's classification of 35 animals shows, the survival of calves (8) and yearlings (7) was encouraging, and the potential for increase (13 females) was apparent. By 1915, the population may have been nearing 100. Known mortality is shown only in 1904. While winter loss probably occurred during other years, the death of many animals would surely have been observed and reported by Army patrols or scouts.

Present composition

An estimate of the contribution of the two subspecies to the present population gene pool is, at best, rough but is preferable to having none. Table 3 shows the sex and adult-calf composition of the fenced herd from 1902 through 1915. The addition to this herd of four calves captured by Army scouts (Fig. 13) from the wild herd for the purpose of adding a second bloodline is also shown. From these numbers, Table 4 was compiled to show the age classes according to sex. The bulls 4 years and older were assumed to have done the breeding in this fenced situation, although younger bulls may have been physically capable. Females were assumed to breed as 2-year-olds and to calve at 3. From these assumptions and the

Fig. 13. Buffalo Jones and Army Scout Holt with a captured bison calf on a sled. Photo from Yellowstone National Park files.

TABLE 3. *Composition of fenced herd, 1902-15*

Year	Males yrlg & over	Females yrlg & over	Total	Male calves	Female calves	Total calves	Herd total	Show herd[b]
1902	3	18	21				21	
1903	2	18	20	2 + 2 wild	3	7	27	
1904	6	20	26	6	6 + 1 wild	13	39	
1905	12[a]	27[a]	39[a]	3[a]	2	5	44	
1906	15[a]	29[a]	44[a]	9[a]	4[a]	13	57	
1907	22[a]	32[a]	54[a]	3[a]	2[a]	5	59	
1908	25[a]	34[a]	59[a]	7[a]	7[a]	14	73	
1909	30[a]	42[a]	72[a]	13 + 1 wild	9	23	96	14
1910	41	51	92[a]	19	9	28	120	16
1911	56[a]	56[a]	112[a]			29	141	15
1912	58	61	119[a]	14	10	24	143	yes
1913	66[a]	66[a]	132[a]	15	15	30	162	yes
1914	77	82	159[a]	20	15	35	194	16 + 20
1915	94[a]	96	190[a]	28	21	49	239	yes

[a]Calculated.
[b]Show herd is included in herd total.

tables, the wild strain in the fenced group was estimated at a maximum of 10% by 1910. Further dilution of the wild strain in the fenced herd was assumed until perhaps 1917.

Sometime between 1915 and 1920, intermingling of the introduced and wild animals began. At first this was probably gradual. Park records do not show the specific year, but after 1915 the close herding practices in use with the introduced herd were abandoned, and the animals were kept on open range all summer. Close account was kept of most of them for several more years, but there were some escapees. After 1921, with construction of a log drift fence across the Lamar Valley above Soda Butte Creek, deliberate efforts were made to keep the introduced herd on the higher summer ranges, where intermingling with the wild bison must have quickly increased.

After intermingling of wild and introduced animals began, several factors tended to increase the wild strain in the total population, although the plains type outnumbered the wild roughly 3:1 about 1917, and perhaps 4:1 in 1921. The number of males in the introduced herd was reduced by the yearly segregation of a show herd of bulls beginning in 1909. Additional bulls were removed by live shipment and slaughter. To further reduce the male surplus (from a ranch operation view-

point), castration of bull calves averaged slightly over 50% from 1916 through 1931. As a result, the number of aggressive, dominant plains-type bulls with the intermingled groups would have been considerably decreased.

Table 5 shows the presumed numbers of freeranging males in various age classes for both wild and introduced herds in 1921. An estimated 40% of the bulls older than 5 years were of the mountain bison strain. Their contribution to the breeding activity may have been larger, as discussed above, than their numbers indicate.

The trend toward increased mountain bison strain would have continued during the 1920s. On this basis, a reasonable estimate of wild strain in the present bison population would seem to be 30-40%.

Numbers and distribution

Management practices for many years made little attempt to re-create a natural, wild bison population in the park. Efforts concentrated on ensuring bison in numbers sufficient to guarantee perpetuation. Through 1938, horseback riders rounded up as many bison as possible in late fall and drove them into the Lamar Valley for feeding and reductions. To cut population numbers to desired levels during these reductions (and in most later ones), cripples,

TABLE 4. *Presumed age and sex composition, fenced herd, 1903-10.*

	Males									Females								
Year Age:	Adult	7	6	5	4	3	2	Yrlg	Calf	Adult	7	6	5	4	3	2	Yrlg	Calf
1903	2-P								2-P 2-W	18-P								3-P
1904	2-P							2-W 2-P	6-P	17-P							3-P	1-W 6-P
1905	2-P						2-W 2-P	6-P	3-P	17-P						3-P	1-W 6-P	2-P
1906	2-P					2-W 2-P	6-P	3-P	9-P	17-P					3-P	1-W 6-P	2-P	4-P
1907					2-W 2-P	6-P	3-P	9-P	3	16-P				3-P	1-W 6-P	2-9	4-P	2
1908				2-W 2-P	6-P	3-P	9-P	3	7	16-P			3-P	1-W 6-P	2-P	4-P	2	7
1909			2-W 2-P	6-P	3-P	9-P	3	7	13 1-W	16-P		3-P	1-W 6-P	2-P	4-P	2	7	9
1910[a]		2-W 2-P	5-P	2-P	7-P	3	6	13 1-W	19	15-P	3-P	1-W 6-P	2-P	4-P	2-P	7	9	9

P — plains type; W — wild type.

[a]For 1910, the number of females, yearlings and older, does not agree with table 3 because of discrepancies in available records.

TABLE 5. *Presumed age classes of male bison on the range, 1921.*

Age classes	Wild herd	Introduced herd
1	7	21
2	5	47
3	4	30
4	3	30
5	2	23
6+	30	47
Total males 1 year and older	51	198[a]
Total population	125 estimated	526

An equal sex ratio is assumed.
[a]Number includes 96 steers among the 1-5 year olds.

aged animals, and those infected with brucellosis or otherwise considered undesirable were removed to improve the herd, in keeping with the ranching viewpoint (W.S. Chapman 1969 pers. comm.). In 1939, a hay-baiting operation was substituted for the roundup. Hay was fed to some extent every winter through 1952. Before 1936, most animals wintered in Lamar, with some in Pelican. During summer, bison concentrated on the Mirror Plateau and Upper Lamar, with scattered bulls and a few small groups to the north. In spite of very large populations wintering in Lamar, natural reestablishment of the population west beyond the Pelican area into Hayden Valley and the Firehole did not occur, although a 1946 file report contains a penciled notation of some bison in Hayden Valley in 1930-31.

In 1936, animals were trucked to the Firehole and Hayden valleys for release. They were thought to have formed separate herds, but as numbers increased, some movement between the two valleys became obvious, and they were called the Mary Mountain herd. Two other herds were distinguished, on the basis of wintering areas, as the Lamar and Pelican. None of these herds is geographically isolated at all seasons of the year, but the names are still used to designate the wintering populations.

Population counts, estimates, and known losses (mainly reductions) are listed in Appendix IV by the three wintering populations and as park totals. Aerial counts were started for the four main wintering valleys (Lamar, Pelican, Hayden Valley, Firehole) in 1949. These counts were not made every year, nor were all main areas checked each time. Usually no attempt was made to count scattered animals in fringe areas, nor to check the Bechler Meadows before 1965 (Jim Stradley 1968 pers. comm.). When aerial counts were not available, winter ground counts were made. Estimates based on previous counts, reduction figures, and presumed increases were made by park personnel when counts were not available. Because of possible population shifts, these may be unreliable. Population numbers are for winter seasons, after reductions, but before calving.

Bison increased steadily after 1902 until, with a gradual change in policy about 1930 from one of ranching to one of preservation of bison in a natural state, the National Park Service decided to cut the numbers wintering in Lamar. The decision was based on the gradual elimination of artificial management practices and supported by information derived from a range-condition and carrying-capacity study (Rush 1932b). Lamar-wintering bison numbered over 1000 from 1929 through 1932, before Rush recommended a maximum of 1000. Later decisions lowered the maximum number until frequent reductions had cut Lamar herd numbers to a count of 143 in 1952. After an aerial count for all main wintering valleys totaled 1477 in January 1954, reductions were made on all population segments. An aerial count for the entire park of 397, made in March 1967, was considered very accurate. Thus, the park population of bison for most of the study period was lower than at any time since the early years of the introduced herd.

Winter and summer distributions for mixed herd groups and separate bulls at population levels of the study period are shown in Table 6. Divisions between major areas indicate geographic separation but do not imply population isolation. Bulls were found in all areas of herd use and also were scattered in places where herd groups were seldom or never seen. Past records indicate that mixed herd groups used some of these areas when population numbers were higher. In effect, places most frequented by mixed herd groups probably represent core areas or population centers from which bulls and mixed herd groups move into less-favored locations as the population increases.

Although Firehole and Hayden valleys are combined as the Mary Mountain area, winter distribution of total numbers and mixed herd groups favored Hayden Valley, according to available counts since the 1950s. During the reductions of 1964-65 and 1965-66, animals were herded from Hayden Valley to the Nez Perce trap on the Firehole side with helicopters, but a prereduction count in December 1964 showed 436 bison in Hayden Valley, and only 54 on the Firehole. Prereduction counts of 1965-66 also located most animals in Hayden Valley. Groups released from the trap usually remained on the west side the rest of the winter, but movements by them between the two wintering valleys were known for all seasons. Groups were seen only in the two main valleys and the intervening Nez Perce Creek drainage during the study period, but a group of 20-23 was seen at Beach or Dryad lakes, 5 miles south of Hayden Valley, the winter of 1955-56 (Jim Stradley 1968 pers. comm.).

The majority of the wintering mixed herd groups of the Mary Mountain area summered in Hayden Valley and to the south of it as far as Beach and Dryad lakes, although some animals from the same population summered to the west of the Firehole. Ranger reports indicate that infrequent mixed herd use of the Madison Plateau began in 1939, 3 years after the bison were released on the Firehole. By the early 1950s, use had become common, but apparently almost ceased after the 1955 reduction. But in 1963 as many as

50 ranged from the Little Firehole Meadows to the Pitchstone Plateau. In spite of more reductions, small mixed herd groups were seen during the summers of 1965, 1966, and 1967.

After the early 1900s, animals were not again reported wintering in the Bechler Meadows southwest of the Madison Plateau until February 1955, when three bulls were seen just outside the park. An occasional bull may have wintered in the meadows earlier, since a few animals again began to summer on the Madison Plateau in 1939. Observations and reports indicate a few animals in that area nearly every winter since the mid-1950s, in spite of considerable decrease in the Mary Mountain herd, from which these animals probably came. No mixed herd groups were reported wintering in the Bechler Meadows until 1962-63, but the area is seldom visited in winter. Periodic plane flights begun in March 1965 showed a small group there in 1964-65 and 1965-66.

Lamar and Pelican populations are isolated from each other during most of the winter except for occasional movements of a few hardy bulls. Table 6 shows the valleys as distinct wintering areas. Groups in Lamar ranged the valley from Soda Butte west to the Hellroaring Slopes. In Pelican, group use extended from the Mushpots-Mudkettles of Pelican Creek downstream to Vermilion Hot Springs and included the lower parts of Astringent Creek and

TABLE 6. *Distribution of the present population, 1969.*

	Winter			Summer	
Bulls	Mixed herd groups			Mixed herd groups	Bulls
Mixed group areas Round Prairie Cache Cr. Slough Cr. Hellroaring-Tower Jct. area	Soda Butte area aupper main Lamar Valley lower main Lamar Valley aHellroaring Slope area	Lamar	Upper Lamar and Mirror Plateau	aMt. Norris Cache-Calfee ridge Miller Cr. ridge Canoe Lake-Hoodoos aSaddle Mt. aLittle Saddle Mt. head of Flint Cr.	mixed group areas widely scattered north of Lamar Valley and on the Mirror Plateau Cache Cr. Miller Cr. along the upper Lamar R.
Mixed group areas Ponuntpa Hot Sp. Heads of Opal and Flint Cr. White Lake Astringent Cr. Upper Pelican Valley Mouth Pelican Cr. Lakeshore from Steamboat Pt. to the Yellowstone R.	aMushpots-Mudkettles main valley from Pelican Sp. to Vermilion Sp. aTurbid Lake area athermal areas west of Astringent Cr.	Pelican		to heads of Pelican, Timothy, Raven Cr. ahead of Opal Cr. ahead of Buffalo Fork of Timothy Cr.	
Mixed group areas East side of Yellowstone R. Mud Volcano Entire main valley Beach Lake	west of Yellowstone River: southwest corner northeast to junction Alum-Violet Cr.	Hayden Valley	Hayden Valley Area	west and southwest part inc. Highland Hot Sp. upper Alum Cr. aupper Trout Cr. acentral valley aupper Nez Perce Cr. upper Spruce Cr. to Beach Lake and area	mixed group areas Cygnet Lakes lower Sour Cr. Arnica Cr.

TABLE 6. (continued) *Distribution of the present population, 1969.*

	Winter		Summer	
	Bulls	Mixed herd groups	Mixed herd groups	Bulls
	Mixed group areas Entire Firehole area from Old Faithful through the Lower Geyser Basin Madison Jct. area Smokejumper Hot Sp.	aupper Nez Perce Cr. lower Nez Perce Cr. entire Lower Geyser Basin aMidway Geyser Basin aBiscuit Geyser Basin	from Little Firehole Mdws. south across Summit Lake area to west end of Pitchstone Plateau aupper Boundary Cr.	Madison and Pitchstone Plateaus	widely scattered
Firehole				
Bechler		Bechler Ford		
Bechler Ford Dunanda Hot Sp.				

aLess used.

adjacent hot-spring areas to the west. Although no groups frequented Ponuntpa Hot Springs (6 miles north of Pelican Valley) during the study, both historic records and reports of the mid-1950s (Jim Stradley 1969 pers. comm.) indicated some previous mixed herd use.

Bison from both Pelican and Lamar Valley wintering populations ranged widely during summers on the Mirror Plateau and the Upper Lamar. Neckband observations and aerial counts showed that the two populations, except scattered bulls, combined on the east boundary for several weeks in 1967. Main use areas in the Upper Lamar region during the study period were the Cache-Calfee and the Miller Creek ridges from the east boundary down, and the series of meadows and parks on the east rim of the Mirror plateau extending from the head of Flint Creek to the heads of Pelican-Timothy-Raven creeks. At higher population numbers, as reports of the 1930s and 1950s indicate, herd-group use included most of Specimen Ridge north and west of Flint Creek as well.

To the north of Lamar Valley, where at present only bulls summer, past reports indicate small mixed herd groups on the upper Slough Creek meadows and the Buffalo Plateau (Jim Stradley, Dave Pierson 1968 pers. comm.). In August 1943, a report was received of an estimated 150 bison

near Lake Abundance, just outside the northeast corner of the park.

Two small areas, separated by distance and topography from the four main valleys, have had small wintering mixed herd groups before the study period, according to recent records. Approximately 40-50 bison wintered north of the Madison River on the flats just southwest of the Cougar Creek patrol cabin in 1955-56. Some were also seen in 1959. In the Antelope Creek basin on the northeast flank of Mount Washburn (no date), 45-70 wintered one year (Jim Stradley 1968 pers. comm.). There were no summer reports of groups north of the Madison River, although the bison wintering there in the 1950s may also have summered there.

Bulls were not distributed proportionately among the four main wintering valleys, as shown in Table 7. Most of the Mary Mountain area bulls wintered in Hayden Valley. Lamar Valley had more bulls than did the Pelican area. In summer, bull distribution was widespread. Animals were so scattered that preference for certain general areas by a large percent of the bulls was not observed.

Recent and present population distributions generally resemble those described by historical sources (Fig. 11). Winter distributions within the park approximate those of early times, as do summer distributions on the Mirror-Upper

TABLE 7. *Comparative distribution of bulls wintering apart from mixed groups.*

Year	Lamar			Pelican			Hayden Valley			Firehole		
	No. bulls	Total pop.	% Bulls	No. bulls	Total pop.	% Bulls	No. bulls	Total pop.	% Bulls	No. bulls	Total pop.	% Bulls
1965-66	36	66	55	29	100	29	–	–	–	–	–	–
1966-67	48	82	56	28	124	23	89	135	66	15	54	26
1967-68	44	89	54	33	160	19	73	131	56	11	57	19

Lamar. Other summer distributions have changed most. The herd which summered north of the Lamar-Yellowstone rivers in historic times is now gone. The large numbers which once ranged the west side (Madison-Pitchstone plateaus) in summer are reduced to comparatively few. The segments of these two historical summer herds which wintered beyond the park boundaries are also gone. The recent Hayden Valley summering population seems larger than the historic population. Bison use of the valley may actually have increased, compared to former times, as the population became reestablished. Or the increase may not be real, but may result from incomplete historical information.

Although present winter distributions seem little altered (except in total numbers) compared to historic times, the Firehole population may be larger now. Changes in the summering distributions of Hayden Valley to the east and the Madison-Pitchstone plateaus to the west may have caused changes on the Firehole, or unrecorded poaching in that wintering valley may have resulted in apparent early low numbers.

4
General Characteristics

Physical Characteristics
Appearance

BISON ARE GENERALLY dark brown in color, almost black when a new coat is growing in during summer. The head, forelegs, hump, and shoulders are covered with longer hair (about 6 inches on shoulders and hump), but the hair on the flanks and hindquarters is much shorter (about 1 inch), so that some bison look as though they had been clipped (Fig. 14). As the coat ages, the longer hair over the hump and shoulders may lighten considerably, becoming almost tan on some animals, particularly older bulls. Shedding of old hair begins in spring, but many bison still have ragged patches of lighter-colored, old hair in mid-summer, particularly on the shoulders (Fig. 15). Wisps of this crinkly, shedding hair are commonly seen on trees and bushes (Fig. 16).

Calves are reddish tan at birth (Fig. 17) but begin to lose this first coat and change to brown-black at about 3 months (Fig. 18). By about 5-6 months of age calves are completely dark. The occasional red one seen in the fall is a late-born calf.

Males and females generally resemble each other in color, shape, and presence of permanent horns. Both sexes have the shoulder hump (calves do not) which, together with the longer hair on the foreparts and head, give a massive appearance to the front of the body compared with the hindquarters. Bison are, however, sexually dimorphic (different in appearance); older animals can be differentiated by an observer (Figs. 19-22). Horn size and shape is characteristic; additionally, bulls are larger and the head shape is broader and generally more massive. The contrast between areas of long and short hair on bulls is more marked.

Weight

Weight differences are greatest between male and female adult bison. Weights (except adult bulls) were recorded in Yellowstone during the winters of 1964-65 and 1965-66, when adults weighed less (indicated by sequential winter

Fig. 14. Clipped appearance of a mature bull. Photo by M.D. Beal, Yellowstone National Park.

weight records) than they would in the fall. Estimates of maximum bull weights of 2000 pounds were made by experienced observers. Most adult cows weighed between 800 and 1100 pounds. Yearlings of both sexes usually weighed between 500 and 700 pounds, calves (8-9 months old), between 300 and 400 pounds. Weights at birth have not been recorded here; Park (1969) gives a range of 30-70 pounds.

No record was made of the weight of the Yellowstone bull (Fig. 23) whose skull is still the largest listed in the records of the Boone and Crockett Club (1964). This animal, a member of the Buffalo Ranch herd (see History) was shot in 1925 after he became too dangerous for the semiranching operation of the time. Old park files indicate he was the offspring of one of the plains bison cows which was pregnant when brought to Yellowstone in 1902. Hence this bull was of plains bison stock, rather than a hybrid offspring of plains and mountain bison.

Fig. 15. Bison shedding old hair, mid-summer.

Fig. 16. Wisps of shed bison hair on a branch of a lodgepole pine.

Fig. 17. Newly-born calves in a mixed herd group. Photo by Verde Watson, Yellowstone National Park.

Fig. 18. The calf (5-6 months old) to the left of the cow has lost its first red-brown pelage. Photo by David Condon, Yellowstone National Park.

Fig. 19. Note head shape and relative size of the cow, left center, compared with the bull at right. Photo by David Condon, Yellowstone National Park.

Fig. 20. Spike-horn bull, approximately 2.5 years old. Photo by David Condon, Yellowstone National Park.

Fig. 21. Standing animals, from left: spike-horn bull, yearling female (approximately 1.5 years old), cow, cow, cow, bull. Photo by David Condon, Yellowstone National Park.

Fig. 22. The horns of the adult cow (at right) are relatively slender compared with those of bulls. The spike-horn bull at left is approximately 3.5 years old. Photo by David Condon, Yellowstone National Park.

Fig. 23. Old Tex, the Yellowstone bull whose head is still first among record bison heads listed by the Boone and Crockett Club (1964). Photo by James Kimberlin, Yellowstone National Park.

Life span

Longevity in a wild bison population is usually less than that of animals in zoos and other protected circumstances. Longevity may also vary among wild populations. In Yellowstone, relatively few members of the population attain old age, which probably begins at 12-15 years of age (Fuller 1959). An occasional one of these aged bison is probably more than 20 years old (from Yellowstone trap records of 1964-65 and 1965-66).

Behavior Characteristics
Grouping characteristics

Bison are gregarious animals usually found in groups of various sizes, although there are scattered solitary bulls at all season. The vast herds (of plains bison) commonly mentioned by historians are not seen in Yellowstone. Small bands, typical of the original mountain bison population (as described by early travelers), are also characteristic at present. During the higher population levels of the 1950s, McHugh (1958) found that cow (mixed) group size ranged from 10 to 50 in Lamar during the winter, with a mean of 20. During the rut in Hayden Valley, he observed a range of 19-480, with a mean of 175.

At population levels of the present study, small winter groups were also characteristic; during

summer, groups of more than 100 were rare. The occasional melding of smaller herd units into a much larger group usually resulted from disturbance by people or aircraft. Typically, even when 100 or more animals were in sight at once in Hayden Valley during the summer, they were in two or more subunits which were often close together, but did not actually form one large herd. However, during the rut, the subunits sometimes melded although they were not disturbed.

Although mature bulls were commonly seen in the mixed groups at all seasons, many bulls were separate from these groups. Some bulls (not always old animals) were solitary, but pairs and small groups up to four and five were common, particularly in winter. Occasionally a cow was seen with a bull group. Such cows were without calves at the time, but were not always old or barren as McHugh observed. Younger cows were seen in bull groups several times; one (a crippled cow) was seen with a calf after wintering with a bull group.

Small bands appear to be the basic population unit, but the nature of these bands is not clear. Fuller (1960) considered the observations of various writers and concluded that there was a basic unit of some sort, centering around 11-20 individuals. McHugh (1958) concluded that subgroup and group formation was flexible, with little dependence on blood relationship (except the cow with calf).

Behavior in specific circumstances

Historical references often mention that bison face into the wind during snowstorms. This may have been very common among plains bison when no shelter was available. Conditions which prevail during severe snowstorms in Yellowstone permitted few observations during this study, but bison, when visible at all, were not seen standing head into the wind. Rather, they were bedded in the snow, usually in whatever protection small variations in terrain offered. At times they were seen moving with the wind, sometimes into the trees at the edges of the wintering valleys. Dave Pierson (1971 pers. comm.) states that during the Buffalo Ranch operation in Lamar he often saw bison on the open feedgrounds facing into the most severe winter storms.

During the breeding season (rut), bulls engaged in considerable head shoving, but actual battles were never witnessed. Fuller (1960) witnessed shoving matches between bulls, but most encounters were decided by threats. McHugh (1958) described battles but did not state that these were between unfenced bison bulls. The bulls do a great deal of bellowing, along with horning of trees and ground, and more wallowing than is observed at other times. Bulls do not dominate groups of cows as a harem unit, as do elk (*Cervus canadensis*), but are usually part of a mixed herd group along with other bulls of various ages. There was no evidence from this study that solitary bulls were forced away from mixed groups.

Bison are very agile, being able and willing to traverse fallen trees and steep slopes with speed. They are capable of a top speed of 30-35 mph (Fuller 1960) and are strong swimmers. Although large, they readily disappear in the forest, blending with the darkness of lodgepole pines.

Senses and disposition

Bison use the senses of smell, hearing, and sight. The sense of smell is well developed, and bison reaction to the odor of an observer is often more marked than reaction to sight or sound. Bison are typically alert and are wary of an observer whether seen or heard, but a careful approach to a viewpoint is often possible if the wind has not carried the scent to them. After an observer is scented, flight is usually immediate for at least a short distance.

Sight more frequently causes flight than does sound, and an observer sighted on foot is more disturbing than one on horseback.

TABLE 8. *Opportunities to see bison from present park roads.*

Time of year	Location and frequency			
	Bulls		Herd groups	
Winter, spring (thru May)	Lamar: west of Lamar Canyon and Soda Butte	daily	Lamar: especially west of Lamar Canyon	frequently
	ªFirehole Geyser Basins	daily	ªLower Geyser Basin	frequently
	ªHayden Valley	daily		
	ªMary Bay	daily		
June	Hayden Valley	occasionally	Same as above in early June only	frequently
	Firehole, particularly the Lower Geyser Basin and near Old Faithful	frequently		
	Mary Bay	early June only		
July, early August	Hayden Valley	frequently		not seen
Mid-August to mid-September	Lower Geyser Basin	frequently		not seen
	Hayden Valley	frequently		
	Lamar	occasionally		
After mid-September	Same as above		Lower Geyser Basin	occasionally
Late fall (roads still open to conventional vehicles)	Lower Geyser Basin	frequently	Lower Geyser Basin	frequently
	Hayden Valley	frequently	Lamar	occasionally
	Mary Bay	frequently	Hayden Valley	rarely

ªVia oversnow vehicle until the roads are plowed in the spring.

Note: In the Lower Geyser Basin, two side roads—Fountain Flat and Firehole Lake—in addition to the main road all provide opportunities to see bison.

In winter a skier is usually detected as soon as in view of a herd, although the skier may be a mile or more away. However, if the skier uses white clothing, approach to less than 100 yards is sometimes possible unless scent disturbs the bison.

One exception to the usual wariness of bison is common. Solitary bulls are probably as aware of an observer in a given set of circumstances as is a group of bison. However, these bulls are much more inclined to stand their ground, particularly near roads, where they are more accustomed to people. Their tolerance of approach is misleading; they are not aggressive, but when approach is beyond tolerance, they will depart. The line of departure may be through or over unwary people who sometimes nearly surround one of these bulls.

Observations made during this study concur with those of Fuller (1960), who reported that bison were neither aggressive nor unpredictable. He characterized the mixed herds as usually shy and timid and used the term "stolid indifference" for the bull groups. All bison should be viewed from a respectful distance.

Visitor opportunities to see bison

Bison behavior and habits (see Movements) influence opportunity to see them from park roads (Table 8). Such viewing is best done from a vehicle, to minimize disturbing the animals and destroying the opportunity for others to watch.

The visitor who is able and willing to penetrate the wilderness of Yellowstone on foot or horseback may, with luck, see the herd groups on their summer ranges. The herd groups in Yellowstone can be characterized as very elusive and very mobile, and a sight of them is not always possible even for the experienced observer. But the opportunity to watch a group of truly wild bison, living as they have for generations in this high mountain wilderness, is an experience to be remembered and cherished.

5
Population Characteristics

THIS CHAPTER DISCUSSES THE REPRODUCTION and population structure and dynamics of Yellowstone bison during the period 1964-68. A series of bison reductions from 1961 through 1965 consistently removed a large number of breeding-age females. Records indicate that the reductions by field shooting of the mid-1950s also did this, as did some of the earlier removals at the Buffalo Ranch in Lamar (Table 9). Some population characteristics may change after a period without reductions . Data for all categories were not obtainable each year; hence, selected figures are used in some instances to suggest population conditions.

Sexual Maturity

Incidence of pregnancy by age class for two Yellowstone studies 25 years apart are compared in Table 10 as an indication of sexual maturity in the female population. The 1940-41 study sampled the semiranched population of La-

mar; the 1964-66 study sampled the entire free-ranging population. The rates of pregnancy in the younger age classes are suggestive only, due to limited sampling. The 1940-41 study of the semidomestic herd indicated that an occasional female bred as a yearling. None (of 15 sampled) was found to be pregnant in the later study of wild bison. The 1964-66 study indicated that a few more bred as 2-year-olds and that approximately a fourth of the 3-year-olds were breeding. Both studies showed that the majority of females attained sexual maturity when 4 years old.

Sexual maturity for the female population as a whole may be occurring somewhat later now. The 1964-66 study of wild bison showed fewer females pregnant in the 3.5 and 4.5 age classes (27 and 71%, respectively) compared with 1940-41 study of the semidomesticated bison (50 and 92%, respectively).

Sexual maturation also may be later in the Yellowstone population of this study compared with herds elsewhere. At Wood Buffalo National Park, 36% (160 sampled) of the Hay Camp and 59% (17 sampled) of the Lake Claire 2-year-olds were pregnant. Rates were 52% at both locations (92 and 31 sampled, respectively) for 3-year-olds (Fuller 1962). At Wichita, 74% (35 sampled) of the 3-year-old cows had calves (Halloran 1968).

Sexual maturity of males was not studied in Yellowstone. However, Fuller (1962) found that examination for spermatogenesis showed the age for males to be comparable to that for females: a few mature as yearlings, a third as 2-year-olds, and probably all others by 3 years of age. Halloran (1968) found that two experimental bulls were effective sires as 2-year-olds. According to observations made by McHugh (1958) in Hayden Valley in Yellowstone, males 8 years and older were the most active sexually, as indicated by "tending bonds"—the term he used for the relationship between a bull and a particular cow during the rut. Fuller (1960) also observed that only fully mature males tended cows. Apparently, sexual maturity in males occurs well before they are a part of the active breeding population.

Reproduction Rate

The present wild population showed a lower pregnancy rate in all age classes over 2.5 years compared with the semidomesticated herd of 1940-41 (Table 10). Females 3.5 years of age and older averaged 56 and 90%, respectively. Females 4.5 years and older averaged 62 and 90%, respectively.

Table 11 compares reproductive data recorded at Lamar by Rush (1932a), several later unpublished compilations also made at Lamar, and this study of the entire population. The pregnancy rate of 52% for females 2.5 years of age and older determined in this study was the lowest recorded in Yellowstone. The reason for this was not clear, because the age classes represented in all previous compilations (except 1940-41) were not recorded. The rate of 65% in 1931-32, which was lower than others prior to this study, may reflect a high percentage of aged females in that sample, as few cows were removed from the semi-domestic herd before 1930. The influence of ranching practices such as winter feeding and culling of aged animals for many years may account for subsequent high pregnancy rates.

Yellowstone's present wild bison population showed a reproductive rate equal to the 52% reported by Halloran (1968), and lower than the rate among all populations compared by Fuller (1962). Halloran attributed the low rate at Wichita Mountains Wildlife Refuge to high calf survival. Calves were known to nurse into their

TABLE 9. *Number of cows and calves removed during reductions.*

Year	Location	Cows		Calves		bTotal no. classified	Percent of reduction
		No.	Percent of total classified	No.	Percent of total classified		
1931-32	Lamar	184	90	1		205	92
1932-33	Lamar	90	45	0		199	96
1933-34	Lamar	59	85	0		69	39
1938-39	Lamar	9	13	0		67	100
1940-41	Lamar	110	54	0		205	100
1941-42	Lamar	78	39	41	21	200	100
1943-44	Lamar	219	55	90	22	400	99
1945-46	Lamar	94	47	20	10	200	100
1949-50	Lamar	129	57	39	17	228	100
1953-54	Lamar	34	45	13	17	75	100

TABLE 9. (continued) *Number of cows and calves removed during reductions.*

Year	Location	Cows		Calves		[b]Total no. classified	Percent of reduction
		No.	Percent of total classified	No.	Percent of total classified		
1955-56	Lamar	15	62	2	8	24	100
	[a]Mary Mountain	123	53	59	26	231	100
	[b]Pelican	53	45	32	27	118	100
1956-57	Lamar	29	49	13	22	59	100
	[a]Mary Mountain	93	44	43	20	212	100
1961-62	Lamar	74	52	33	23	143	100
1962-63	Mary Mountain	187	52	101	28	357	100
1964-65	Lamar	42	51	6	7	82	100
	Mary Mountain	119	50	39	12	238	100
	[a]Pelican	14	41	8	24	34	100
1965-66	Mary Mountain	18	36	9	18	50	100

[a]Field shooting.
[b]Total classified (bulls, steers, cows, calves) not necessarily total reduction number.

TABLE 10. *Comparison of female pregnancy rates, by age classes, 1940-41 and 1964-66.*

Age class	No. sampled		Percent pregnant	
	1940-41[a]	1964-66	1940-41[a]	1964-66
2.5	2	7	0	14
3.5	4	11	50	27
4.5	13	7	92	71
Young adult	10	6	100	50
Adult	49	23	86	57
Aged	8	17	100	75
Entire sample	86	71	86	52

[a]From Skinner, Curtis K. 1941. Special report on Yellowstone National Park bison. Yell. Natl. Park Bio. Files, 715-03. Buffalo (General). Typed.

second year of life, thus prolonging the physical drain on the cows (and perhaps influencing the possibility of conception). Fuller considered brucellosis infection and severe climate as possible adverse influences on reproductive rates in Wood Buffalo National Park.

Calf survival apparently was not an important influence on the reproductive rate determined by the present study. Although survival appeared high (see Calf Mortality), no yearlings were observed nursing during the study. Only 4% of the cows (Table 11) examined during the mid-winter reductions were still lactating.

Brucellosis in Yellowstone animals did not appear to be a factor in the low incidence of pregnancy. Rate of infection according to tests from 1964-66 averaged about 54% for Lamar, 42% for Pelican, and 26% at Nez Perce Creek in the Firehole area (Barmore 1968). These rates were all lower than the 62% at Lamar in 1941 when the pregnancy rate, at 86%, was much higher than now. Although Rush (1932a) mentions that a number of abortions were known to have occurred, abortions were apparently rare except in the crowded corral at the Buffalo Ranch (Dave Pierson 1968 pers. comm.). Quortrup (1945) stated that brucellosis had little or no effect on the herds, as did Tunnicliff and Marsh (1935) and McKenney (Skinner 1941).

TABLE 11. *Summary of reproductive data and fetal sex ratios, 1931-32 through 1964-66.*

Year	Source	Number sampled	Total pregnant percent	Pregnant and lactating percent	Pregnant only percent	Lactating only percent	Number sampled	Fetal sex ratio male/female	Percent unclassified
1931-32	Rush, 1932a	184	65	52	12	24	54	108/100	—
1940-41	Skinner, 1941	86	86	—	—	5	74	163/100	1
1943-44	Yell. Natl. Park files	219	75	—	—	—	—	—	—
1945-46	Yell. Natl. Park files	82[a]	79	—	—	—	62	112/100	5
1949-50	Yell. Natl. Park files	115	94	—	—	—	104	138/100	1
1964-66	Present Study[b]	71	52	3	50	1	—	—	—

[a]Sample included only females 4 years of age and older. Other samples included some females in the younger age classes.
[b]This study sampled the entire population. Previous studies sampled only Lamar.

Differences in population age structure, as reflected in the samples, partly explain differences in reproductive rates between the wild bison popultions of Wood Buffalo and Yellowstone National parks. Subadults and young adults formed a much larger part of the Wood Buffalo National Park samples (Fuller 1962); aged animals formed more of the Yellowstone sample. However, all age classes (except the aged) in Yellowstone showed a lower reproductive rate.

The low reproductive rate in Yellowstone may result from a complex of environmental factors, in part related to severity of the winters. Both Yellowstone and Wood Buffalo National parks have severe winter conditions, but the details differ (Table 12). Fuller (1962) believed extreme cold, per se, had little effect on bison, but was important when there was wind. Wood Buffalo National Park, compared with Yellowstone, is colder, but has less snow and fewer periods of crusting conditions during the winter. Trees provide protection from the wind. Differences in amount of wind were not as apparent. Yellowstone apparently has a more severe winter environment, for bison, than does Wood Buffalo National Park.

The effects of the Yellowstone winters on subadults is suggested by the mortality among them, as discussed later. Winter conditions, perhaps through nutritional influences, may delay sexual maturity among subadults. Houston (1968) suggested that animal nutrition during winter periods might control yearling moose (*Alces alces*) ovulation rates. Robinette et al. (1955) attributed reproductive rates among yearling mule deer (*Odocoileus hemionus*) to the type of winter preceding that during which the pregnancy rates were determined. Possible variation in effects between mild and severe Yellowstone winters was not obtained during this study.

The influence of Yellowstone winters on reproductive rates among adult bison was unknown. Pregnancy rates among adult moose in Jackson Hole, south of Yellowstone, approximated those from other ranges (Houston 1968). Other environmental factors which were not apparent from this comparison of Yellowstone and Wood Buffalo National parks may be important in affecting adult reproductive rates.

Fetal Sex Ratio

The fetal sex ratio was not estimated during this study. However, records kept by Rush (1932a) and during four later reductions in Lamar (Table 11) showed more males among fetuses, ranging from 108 to 163 males/100 females and averaging 127 males/100 females (294 fetuses). This was slightly higher than the 112 males/100 females reported by Fuller (1962).

TABLE 12. *Comparison of winter climatic factors in Wood Buffalo and Yellowstone National Parks.*

	Cold	Snowfall	Crusting	Wind	Wind protection
Wood Buffalo National Park[a]	January mean daily maximum −7.8° F	53"	apparently rare	rarely over 15 mph in extreme cold	woods everywhere interspersed with grazing areas
Yellowstone National Park[b]	January mean daily maximum approx. 22° F	approx. 150"	most winters, one or more periods	a winter average of more than 8.5 mph	no interspersed woods (except the Firehole), winter valleys large and open

[a]Information from Fuller, W. A. 1962. The biology and management of the *Bison* of Wood Buffalo National Park. Can. Wildl. Serv. Wildl. Manage. Bull. Ser. 1, No. 16, 52 p.
[b]Information from U.S. Dep. Commer. Climatological Summary for Yellowstone National Park (1930-59). Temperatures and snowfall are for the park interior.

Number of Young at Birth

No twin fetuses were noted in any of the above records. One instance of twins in the Lamar herd was reported (McHugh 1958). Other workers (Fuller 1962; Halloran 1968) and historical accounts agree that twins are rare.

Population Structure

Sex and age structure was suggested mainly by trap records made during live-trapping operations from late December to late February in the winter of 1964-65, and from mid-January to mid-March 1966. Efforts were made to trap as many of the Lamar (Crystal trap) and Mary Mountain (Nez Perce trap) animals as possible. More were trapped during the severe winter of 1964-65 than in 1966. Trapping success for calves of the previous spring was nearly 100%, as indicated by comparison of 1964-65 Mary Mountain early winter aerial count records (72 calves) and Nez Perce trap records (77 calves). Most yearlings were probably trapped. Success (indicated by the temporary backtags and the number of retrapped animals) was high in the 2.5- and 3.5-year-old classes, but a few undoubtedly were not taken. Most adult females were trapped; trap success was lowest for males of age classes above 3.5 years, particularly in 1966. That year only 7% of all captures older than 3.5 years were males, compared with 37% in 1964-65 (Nez Perce trap). In addition to the influence of snow depth on trap success, animals trapped the previous year seemed harder to herd.

Age classes for all females trapped (Table 13) provided population sex-ratio information for animals less than 4.5 years of age. The records for all traps suggest that a slightly higher percentage of female calves survive their first year than do males, but the pooled data for yearlings and 2.5-year-olds suggest no further differential loss for this period. The variability, when individual trap records are compared, among the percentages of females in the 2.5- and 3.5-year-old classes may reflect the removal of calves in reductions of 1961-62 (Lamar) and 1962-63 (Mary Mountain). Although this may explain the very low percent of 3.5-year-old females taken at the Lamar trap, all trap records suggest that fewer females survive in this age group. Thus, female survival may be favored the first year, but male survival may be favored the next 3 years of life. Fuller (1960) also noted more males than females in the spike-horn, or 2.5- to 3.5-year-old group, but believed the identifications were biased. By 4.5 years of age and older, differential survival cannot be distinguished from differential trap success.

Trap records, together with the

TABLE 13. *Age classes of bison trapped, reductions of 1964-66.*

Age Class	Lamar 1964-65				Nez Perce 1964-65				Nez Perce 1965-66				Totals for both traps 1964-66			
	Females		Class		Females		Class		Females		Class		Females		Class	
	No.	%	No.	% Trap Total	No.	%	No.	% Trap Total	No.	%	No.	% Trap Total	No.	%	No.	% Trap Total
Calf	13	52	25	19	45	58	77	24	13	59	22	22	71	57	124	22
Yearling	10	53	19	14	26	50	52	16	11	44	25	25	47	51	96	17
2.5	4	40	10	6	17	68	25	8	3	27	11	11	24	52	46	8
3.5	3	21	14	11	8	42	19	6	5	45	11	11	16	37	44	8
Adult	34	53	64	49	97	63	154	47	28	93	30	30	159	64	248	44
Totals	64	49	132	100[a]	193	59	327	100[a]	60	60	99	100[a]	317	57	558	100[a]

[a]Apparent errors in totals are due to rounding.

early-winter aerial count of 480 animals, indicated that adult bulls outnumbered adult cows in the Mary Mountain population of 1964-65. The actual ratio could not be determined, but a minimum bull population of 150 was estimated from the number of trapped bulls removed (48), the scattered bulls in Hayden Valley which could not be driven toward the trap (53), and the number of bulls among the remaining 100 animals never trapped (50 bulls estimated). Because there were probably adult cows as well as some subadults of both sexes among the other 50 animals (of the 100 never trapped), bulls probably totaled less than 60% of the adult population. More bulls than cows could be expected in both the Lamar and Mary Mountain populations after the reductions of the early 1960s removed large numbers of adult cows. The normal proportion may be the reverse; adult cows may outnumber adult bulls. Fuller (1960) believed this to be the situation among the wild bison of Wood Buffalo National Park. Adult male bison may be "biologically expendable" according to Etkin (1964), who states that sexual dimorphism (termed aggressive potential in bison) interferes with male survival.

Age classes were calculated for the Mary Mountain population, using the Nez Perce trap records of 1964-65 and the prereduction

count of 480 bison. Mary Mountain herd records were used, rather than pooled data, because trapping success was high (68%), the sample was largest, and trapping operations were preceded by a careful aerial census for the entire Firehole-Hayden Valley area. The calculations suggested a winter population consisting of: calves, 16%; yearlings, 11%; 2.5-year-olds, 6%; 3.5-year-olds, 5%; and adults, 62%. The extent to which these percentages differ from those of a Yellowstone population not influenced by reductions is not known.

Calf Percentages

Spring calf numbers, calculated as percentages of mixed herds (Table 14) from aerial surveys made in late May and early June 1964 through 1968 after most calves were born, showed considerable variation because of reduction programs. The lowest percentages recorded during the study for Lamar, Pelican, and Mary Mountain were 7, 14, and 7%, respectively, during the spring of 1965 after reductions in all three areas removed large numbers of cows. Thereafter, all percentages increased. By 1968 the Pelican population, where the fewest cows were removed showed what may be a nearly "normal" (uninfluenced by reductions) 18% calves. The higher percentages in Lamar

TABLE 14. *Calf percentages of mixed herd numbers in spring.*

Year	Lamar No. sampled[a]	Lamar % Calves	Pelican No. sampled[a]	Pelican % Calves	Mary Mountain No. sampled[a]	Mary Mountain % Calves	All herds No. sampled[a]	All herds % Calves
1964	43	19	–	–	–	–	43	19
1965[b]	43	7	69	14	67	7	179	10
1966[c]	40 est.	15 est.	–	–	109	12	149	13
1967	31	19	133	15	177	24	341	20
1968	34	27	111	18	48	25	262	19

[a]Number sampled does not correspond with the actual population.
[b]Reductions in all areas.
[c]Reduction in Mary Mountain herd.

(27%) and Mary Mountain (25%) for 1968 probably reflect the higher pregnancy rate of an increased proportion of younger females. Although the number of animals sampled was not large, the 1968 samples represented 95, 75, and 40% of the Pelican, Lamar, and Mary Mountain mixed herd groups.

Pooled percentages for the three herds in 1967 (20%) and 1968 (19%) suggest a leveling in calf production for the population as a whole. If so, then the usual proportion of newly born calves in mixed herds of Yellowstone bison may be 18-20%. Additional data, free from possible reduction influences, are needed to verify this.

Spring calves as a percentage of the total population (mixed herd groups, bull groups, and scattered animals) were calculated only in 1967 from a very accurate (397 count, 400 estimate) census of the entire park just before calving season. Calves formed only 11% of the 1967 spring total population, compared with 20% of the mixed herd groups. Although, as previously discussed, 20% calves in mixed herd groups may be nearly normal, 11% calves among the total population may be low. Reductions have removed a larger proportion of mixed herd animals than of bull groups and scattered animals. As a result, the total of mixed herd groups may form a smaller part of the 1967 population than it would of a population

uninfluenced by recent reductions.

Mortality
Calf mortality

The expected number of calves from the 28 females of breeding age released from the traps during the reduction of 1964-65, using the observed pregnancy rate of 52%, was 15. The actual number seen in those groups in the spring of 1965 was eight. The difference probably represented loss of embryos or neonates. A realistic percentage of such loss for the entire population could not be judged from the limited information.

Field observations of the relatively small bison population of the study period suggested that little additional calf mortality took place before late the following winter (March and early April). Throughout 1966 and 1967, during and after calving season in Lamar and Pelican, periodic ground and aerial checks were made. The agreement on total number of calves seen was quite consistent. Size and color of calves helped to confirm that loss, balanced by addition of some late calves, was not occurring. Calf percentages of herd numbers throughout the year (Table 15) were inconclusive, showing increases in 1965 and 1966, and slight decreases in 1964, 1967, and 1968. Size of some of the samples, skill of the observers, and variable

TABLE 15. *Calf percentages of pooled mixed herd numbers throughout the year.*

Pop. year[b]	Spring		Summer		Fall		Winter	
	No. sampled[b]	% Calves	No. sampled[b]	% Calves	No. sampled[b]	% Calves	No. sampled[c]	% Calves
1963	—	—	908	17	—	—	—	—
1964	43	19	660	18	427	17	—	—
1965	179	10	591	13	242	17	—	—
1966	149	13	1533	19	121	20	165	21
1967	341	20	1724	19	78	18	40	18
1968	262	19	1003	18	—	—	—	—

[a]Population year includes spring, summer, and fall of the year shown, and winter of the following calendar year.
[b]Number sampled does not correspond with the actual population.

conditions of weather and animal visibility may have affected the quality of the counts. The percentages did suggest that there was no appreciable calf loss. Trap records for 1964-65 from Nez Perce showed a ratio of 61 calves per 100 cows (2.5 years of age and older) in winter, although among cows removed from the same population that winter the pregnancy rate was 51%. The sampling may have been biased, the previous year's pregnancy rate may have been higher (unlikely because of a large reduction in 1962-63), or mortality may have occurred in older age classes, but calf mortality was not indicated. In contrast, Fuller (1962) found a steady decline in calf percentages from a peak of 23% of herd numbers in July to less than 10% by the end of the calendar year.

Subadult mortality

Trap records (Table 13) suggested considerable mortality among subadults. The records show that a progressive decline in numbers occurred between calf and yearling, and between yearling and 2.5-year-old age classes. One exception, an increase in percentage of yearlings compared with calves at the Nez Perce trap in 1965-66, may have been caused by a shift of a mixed herd group from one winter range to another. Previous reductions (1961-62 in Lamar;

1962-63 at Nez Perce) may have affected the size of some age classes, but do not explain the similar pattern of percentages among subadult age classes recorded at both traps in 1964-65.

The calculated age classes of the 1964-65 Mary Mountain winter population (16% calves, 11% yearlings, 6% 2.5-year-olds, 67% older) suggested that half the calves which survive into their first winter die before 2.5 years of age. Calf numbers indicated a potential 16% increase. Realized percentages for yearlings and 2.5-year-olds were 13% (11/84) and 8% (6/73), respectively. These indicate a 19% loss between the first and second winters, and a 31% loss between the second and third winters. This mortality most likely occurs in late winter (March and early April) at the end of the first and second years of life, rather than early in winter during the second and third years of life (see Other Mortality).

Variation in subadult mortality rates probably occurs, but cannot be judged from the limited data. Previous reductions, as discussed above, probably had less influence on subadult mortality than did environmental factors. Because this population had not been subject to an unusually severe winter for several years, these percentages may approximate usual mortality among these age groups.

Other mortality

Natural mortality recorded during the study period totaled 49 animals. All but one occurred during the winter after considerable snow had accumulated, usually after January. The number of recorded deaths were 38, 4, 3, and 3 for the winters of 1964-65 (a severe winter), 1965-66, 1966-67, and 1967-68, respectively. With the exception of a small mixed herd group (18 animals), all dead animals were found scattered on the winter ranges. Of the other 30 recorded deaths, there were 22 aged bulls, 2 cows, 3 yearlings, 1 calf, and 2 unknown. More bulls may have been found because of larger carcass size. Reductions, by removal of mixed herd animals, may have substituted for proportionately more natural mortality among cows and younger animals than among bulls.

Natural mortality recorded annually over mild and average winters of the study period averaged less than 1% of the winter herd numbers. One or two animals, usually bulls, were the most found dead in any one of the main wintering valleys. This was also the usual number found before the study period, according to earlier ranger reports, although population numbers varied considerably (Appendix IV). The amount of natural mortality associated with a severe winter such as 1964-65 was obscured by concurrent reduction programs, but the number of dead animals found indicated greatly increased mortality.

Population Trends

Figure 24 shows population trends based on actual counts (postreduction, precalving) from 1936 through 1968 for the entire park, as well as for the wintering subunits of Lamar, Pelican, and Mary Mountain. Known losses, mainly reductions, are also shown. The reductions, held only in Lamar prior to 1954, accounted for the general downward trend in that area, although at the same time the population as a whole increased, influenced mainly by the steady increase of the Mary Mountain herd as it repopulated an area uninhabited by bison for more than 40 years. The peak population in the latter herd and for the total bison population in 1954 apparently coincided with increased use of the Madison Plateau-Pitchstone Plateau summer range, as mixed herd groups were small and infrequently reported from this area for nearly 15 years after the 1936 reintroduction on the Firehole. During the early 1950s, ranger reports indicate yearly use by mixed herds, sometimes large in size. In June 1952, 124 adults and 11 calves were seen.

Since the 1954 peak, all population segments have decreased.

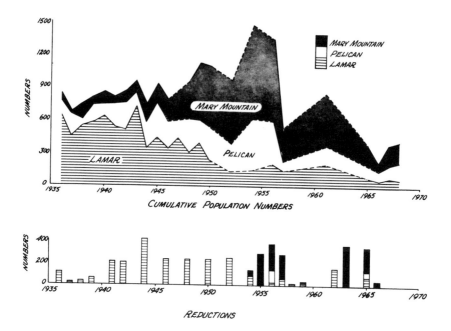

Fig. 24. Bison population trends from population counts, 1936-68.

The 1955 reduction in the Mary Mountain area may have started the downward trend shown between the counts of 1954 and 1956. The marked decrease in population numbers in the Mary Mountain and Pelican herds, and the smaller decrease in Lamar cannot be entirely due to the reductions of 1956; there was none in Pelican. The decrease coincided with the severe winter of 1955-56, when snows were exceptionally heavy in January, and severe cold was prolonged in February. A large winter loss that year was indicated by sightings of 20-30 dead animals in Pelican during an aerial census of late January 1956 (Jim Stradley 1968 pers. comm.). The following June, 32 dead animals were counted in the main valley (Larry Brown 1969 pers. comm.). Reduction only added impetus, apparently, to a natural occurrence.

Immediate increase in the Lamar numbers followed reductions when population levels remained well over 200 animals, before 1952, by which time the last vestiges of the Buffalo Ranch operation (feeding of hay) ceased. Since then, Lamar has shown only very slow increase, although reductions have been few and comparatively small. Reported natural mortality (an occasional animal) indicated that no more bison than usual died most years. Slight increases which showed in counts of 1956 and 1961 were followed by reductions each time. At least 50% of the 1962 reduction consisted of females (yearlings and older). After the 1965 reduction, only nine females (yearlings and older) and 10 female calves were released. The temporary effect of even small reductions on low population levels was apparent, but some increase (with recruitment of more breeding females into the population) expected by 1968 did not occur. This suggests that some factor, other than reductions, may have retarded increase in this population at levels below 200 animals. The factor may be related to the change to a truly wild population, subject to natural environmental influences.

The Pelican population increased from near extinction about 1900 to an estimated more than 100 animals in the early 1920s. It was subject to reductions only twice, in 1956 and again in 1965. From the early 1920s through 1941, it fluctuated between counts of 100 and 200; for the next 10 years fluctuations were generally between 200 and 300 animals. After the peak count of 461 in 1954, followed by the drop to fewer than 100 in 1957, the population again remained between 100 and 200 animals. The lack of increase over fairly long periods of time suggests some balance exists with environmental factors, in which factors favoring increase are usually offset by mortality factors such as winterkill. The 1954 peak may have occurred with exceptionally favorable influences, which existed only briefly.

The park-wide population counts do not suggest that periodic emigration from Pelican to Lamar or Hayden Valley could account for the long-term stability, although apparently temporary population shifts have occurred (see Mixing of Population Segments). No herd groups were reported in Hayden Valley after 1895 until animals from Lamar were trucked there in 1936. Ranger reports made prior to the study period indicate that reproduction by herd groups in Lamar and Hayden Valley probably accounted for the usual population increases in those areas.

Population estimates for the entire park of 400 and 440 animals in 1967 and 1968, respectively, showed a 10% increment for that period. Reduction effects and insufficient population data precluded calculation of annual increment over a longer period.

Between 1965 and 1968, when the study ended, the bison population for the park as a whole showed only slight increase. Three years had elapsed since a major reduction, and 2 years since a small reduction. The apparent increase in the Mary Mountain herd (Fig. 24) between 1966 and 1967 resulted from use of a low actual count in 1966 rather than the more accurate estimate. In all bison population segments, there is the suggestion of some factor or combination of factors retarding increase, aside from the influence of reductions.

Environmental conditions have continued to exert major influence on the bison populations in conjunction with the activities of man. Population trends (since the near extinction of the original wild population about 1902) apparently reflect, initially, reestablishment of populations on historic ranges which had been uninhabited by any bison for some years (Lamar, Mary Mountain), or where the numbers were very low (Pelican). Increase was rapid under conditions of semidomestication (Lamar), and when favorable environmental conditions combined with availability of an extensive, unin-

habited area (Mary Mountain). Later increases were apparently offset by reductions (Lamar), or by reductions in combination with periodically severe environmental conditions (Pelican, Mary Mountain). At lower population numbers, less severe environmental conditions appear adequate to have offset increases and to have resulted in periods of near stability or very slow increase in all population segments.

Presumably, the original wild bison population which inhabited the Yellowstone area throughout the year lived in some balance with the prevailing environmental conditions of that time. Fluctuations in numbers undoubtedly occurred as favorable conditions alternated with periodically severe winters. The present environment of the bison ranges of the park appears little altered by man's influence (with the possible exception of Lamar Valley), although the numbers of some of the predatory and grazing mammals have decreased. The bison population may be expected to increase in the future (since population numbers of the study period are the lowest in many years after the reductions of the 1960s), but may then establish a state of equilibrium with natural environmental conditions.

6
Mortality Factors

Parasites
Internal parasites

YELLOWSTONE BISON appear comparatively free from internal parasitism. During the present study, parasite investigation centered on the occurrence of lungworm (*Dictyocaulus* sp.), as reported by Meagher (1966). Rate of infection for 185 animals examined was 11.4%. Aged animals, with an incidence of 35%, showed the highest rate of infection, contrary to the situation in cattle, where calves show both higher incidence and intensity of infections. *Dictyocaulus* sp. has been reported from a few animals in Wood Buffalo National Park (Fuller 1961), from the National Bison Range (Locker 1953), from Elk Island National Park (Conner and Cornell 1958), and from a fenced herd in Kansas (Frick 1951).

No other internal parasites were found in the brief examinations made of bison during the present study. Locker (1953) recorded only tapeworms (*Moniezia benedeni*) in Yellowstone bison, occurring randomly among all age groups, at an apparently low intensity of infection. A variety of

internal parasites which have been recorded from other bison herds have not been found here.

External parasites

External parasites were not collected from animals during the study period. Burger (1967a, 1967b, 1969 pers. comm.), who studied biting insects in Yellowstone during 1966 and 1967, reported that mosquitoes (*Aedes* sp.), blackflies (or buffalo gnats), particularly *Simulium venustum*, horse and deer flies (Tabanidae), snipe flies (Rhagionidae), and members of the Muscidae may all have had some association with bison. The last two families were most important.

The genus *Symphoromyia* of the Rhagionidae apparently influenced bison distribution during the summer months (see Summer Range Movements). These small gray flies cling tenaciously, inflict a painful bite, and locally may be very abundant. During the summer, bison are nearly naked, as the newly growing hair is very short, resembling fine, black plush. They are particularly vulnerable to biting insects.

Three genera of Muscidae were associated with bison in Yellowstone. The stable fly (*Stomoxys calcitrans*) and the horn fly (*Haematobia irritans*) were observed feeding on bison with no noticeable effect. The face fly (*Musca autumnalis*) was first collected by Burger in 1967. He suggested that this exotic species, if it becomes established in Yellowstone, could cause eye disorders in bison. He noted evidence of severe conjunctivitis associated with the presence of this fly among bison at the National Bison Range.

Diseases

Disease-caused mortality was not identified in the present wild bison population, although outbreaks of hemorrhagic septicemia in 1912, 1919, and 1922 caused considerable mortality in the introduced herd in Lamar Valley. In two instances during the study, young animals died from causes which were not apparent when ample food was available. One was a yearling female, observed by park personnel for some time, unable to keep up with the herd animals, moving very little, and becoming gradually weaker. The other was a young cow, seen for several days at Old Faithful before she died. Both carcasses were nearly consumed by scavengers before examination was possible, but the fat-depleted bone marrow in both cases indicated very malnourished animals. Neither tuberculosis nor anthrax, which have been important causes of mortality in Wood Buffalo National Park (Fuller 1961; Choquette et al., 1966), have ever been detected in Yellowstone.

Brucellosis (Bang's disease, undulant fever in humans), caused by the bacterium *Brucella abortus*, occurs in the present bison population. Whether the organism was introduced or was endemic among North American bovids is not known; it was first tested for and reported in Yellowstone in 1917. The rate of infection has varied considerably among tests made in different years during reduction operations, and also among the wintering populations of a given year. In 1964-65, 129 animals tested in Lamar, 33 tested in Pelican, and 302 tested at the Nez Perce Creek trap showed rates of 59, 42, and 28%, respectively (Barmore 1968).

Evidence suggests that brucellosis has little effect on the Yellowstone bison. Limited examination of reactors slaughtered during the study period indicated normal pregnancies. Rate of pregnancy was apparently not influenced, as discussed previously. Veterinarians who investigated brucellosis in Yellowstone before the study period agreed that there were no apparent effects on the population (Tunnicliff and Marsh 1935; Skinner 1941; Quortrup 1945). Quortrup mentioned that few abortions were observed and gross lesions were rarely seen at postmortem examinations. Dave Pierson, Buffalo Herder and Animal Keeper over a period of 30 years, believed that observed abortions occurred as a result of the handling of pregnant females in chutes, and their confinement in pens during the reductions held at the Buffalo Ranch (1968 pers. comm.). Quortrup believed that brucellosis had probably existed in the Yellowstone bison for a long time, and that they had acquired a natural immunity.

Investigations among bison have apparently concentrated on the incidence of brucellosis rather than its effects. Most bison herds in the United States are maintained in a brucellosis-free condition as part of the U.S. Department of Agriculture brucellosis control program. In Wood Buffalo National Park in Canada, where the presence of brucellosis was confirmed in 1956, Fuller (1962) considered it a possible influence on conception rate. Choquette et al. (1966) also assumed that brucellosis influenced productivity. Among cattle, effects include abortion of calves, temporary sterility, and lowered milk production (Gilman and McAuliff 1956).

Further studies of brucellosis in bison may indicate that mutual adaptation or equilibrium exists, as between parasites and hosts that have long lived together (Allee et al. 1949). Physiological effects of brucellosis, if any, may contribute to maintenance of the bison population within levels which the habitat can support.

Brucellosis is of economic concern to cattlemen, and of health importance to the general public. It is presumed that bison can transmit brucellosis to cattle, because the causative organism is apparently the same in both species of bovids. Transmission tests have not been made to verify this, but on the basis of the assumption, the National Park Service has cooperated with the Department of Agriculture in brucellosis control among bison. In Yellowstone, cooperation has consisted of vaccination of calves and removal of reactors during reductions (held primarily to cut herd numbers). This cooperation resulted in reduction of animal numbers below the park's management objective at Lamar in 1964-65. No reductions have been held specifically for brucellosis control in Yellowstone.

Participation in brucellosis control in Yellowstone National Park has recently been reevaluated by the National Park Service (Barmore 1968). Present bison management objectives are to maintain a wild population under natural conditions. By order of the Superintendent of Yellowstone National Park, future reductions will be held only when research clearly indicates that compensation for a lack in natural controls is necessary. As an alternative to brucellosis control within the park, the objectives of the Department of Agriculture control program can be met by preventing contact between park bison and domestic livestock beyond the park boundaries (see Movements Beyond Park Boundaries).

Predation

There was no direct evidence for predation on the present herd. Circumstances suggested a grizzly kill of an apparently healthy, mature bull in mid-summer of 1967. Remains of bone and hair indicated the bull died at the edge of a small group of trees in a meadow, south of Hayden Valley. The lack of broken bones, the relatively young age of the animal, and the site of death all suggested a grizzly (*Ursus horribilis*) might have killed the bull. McHugh (1958) also mentioned indirect evidence of grizzly predation. Dave Pierson (1968 pers. comm.) believed both black (*Ursus americanus*) and grizzly bears would take calves in the spring, but calf counts during the study do not indicate much loss. However, such loss might have occurred at or immediately after birth, before the calves were observed with the cows.

Wolves (*Canis lupus*), which are known to prey on bison in Wood Buffalo National Park according to Fuller (1961), are the only other likely predators of bison in Yellowstone. Studies such as that made by Mech (1966) have indicated that effective wolf predation on large mammals results from the cooperative efforts of a pack. During the study period wolves were rare in Yellowstone, with no pack activity.

The observed survival, for a long time, of handicapped or weakened bison provided additional evidence that almost no predation was occurring. In one instance, a cow survived at least 2 years with a useless right foreleg. Although her mobility was impaired, she was usually with other bison, at times a mixed herd, more often with one or more bulls. Only once was she seen unaccompanied, except for her calf of that spring. Solitary animals were also usually free from predation. Old bulls, obviously weak, were often observed for several winter months in nearly the same location along the road in Lamar, until finally they died.

Historical information suggests that even during the early years of the park, when predators, particularly wolves, were more numerous, healthy bison of all ages were relatively safe from attack. Although predation becomes more difficult as the prey species decreases (MacArthur and Connell

1966), the predators in this case had alternate prey (elk) to sustain their numbers as bison decreased (from poaching). If bison had been easy or preferred prey, their increase, once they were protected from poaching, might have been prevented.

Other Causes

Winterkill, probably from the combined effects of climatic stress, forage availability, and physiological condition of individual animals, was the main cause of observed mortality (see Other Mortality). Death usually occurred after prolonged weakening, often in late winter (March and early April). A few animals died annually, but the number increased greatly with severe winters. This suggested that climatic influences (long winters, periods of prolonged cold, deep and sometimes crusted snow) acting directly and indirectly on the bison were the most important mortality factors.

The most apparent direct effect of the winter environment, above the energy levels required to maintain body temperature, was the effort required to travel between foraging areas. In deep snow the mixed herd groups usually traveled in line, plunging to create trenches several feet deep (Fig. 25), frequently for more than a mile. Variations in topography crossed added to their efforts.

Fig. 25. Trench left in soft snow by traveling bison.

Observations during the mild and average winters of the study period indicated that snow depth did not limit forage availability. Bison commonly cleared fairly deep snow (by swinging the head in a sideways motion) with apparent ease (Figs. 26, 27). McHugh (1958) observed bison feeding in snow up to 4 feet deep. At higher population levels, snow depth may limit access to forage. However, the size and location of the most used foraging areas suggested that this might happen only under the most extreme conditions (see Use of Forage Areas).

Susceptibility to winterkill varied according to physical condition, as would be expected. Aged animals found dead in mild and average winters indicated that they were most susceptible. Crippled and otherwise handicapped animals, and those weaker because of size, would also be affected more quickly. Differential and total mortality among subadults, as discussed previously, suggested that among otherwise healthy bison of all ages they were most vulnerable. Size, together with social standing in the population (see Suggested Mechanisms of Population Regulation), may explain this.

A quick-acting type of winterkill occurred once during the study period, but old bison bones indicated similar occurrences in the past. During the severe winter of 1964-65, a group of 18 bison (including 3 calves, 2 mature and 1 spike bull, 7 cows of various ages, and 5 unidentified animals) died before the end of January at a small warm-slough area in the Bechler Meadows. The snow there, west of the Continental Divide,

Fig. 27. Feeding site in snow approximately 2 feet deep.

was too deep that winter to allow the animals to move away from the slough area, and presumably they starved to death when the small amount of feed was gone. The slough area apparently becomes a unique trap in severe winters, since 13 other bison survived in Bechler that year, near the slough but along the river banks where movement was possible in the open water.

Accidents accounted for the deaths of a few individuals of all ages nearly every year, as indicated by ranger reports. Most commonly animals drowned in bog holes or fell into hot pools. The accidental death of whole groups while crossing thin river ice has been reported twice. At Slough Creek in 1941, seven yearlings and 2-year-olds died. In 1946, near the Mud Volcano, in the Yellowstone River, 39 died (including 5 calves, 9 yearlings, 6 two-year-olds, 2 mature bulls, 16 mature cows, and 1 unidentified animal).

Fig. 26 Bull bison foraging in snow approximately 2.5 feet deep.

7
Habits

Calving

COMPARISON OF RECORDS kept during the study period with earlier information suggested that the onset of the calving season is later than formerly. From 1937 to about 1950, the first calves were regularly reported in Lamar before mid-April. Since 1950, first calves have all been reported later. McHugh (1958) reported that calving season extended from 15 April to 31 May, with more births the first 2 weeks of May. During the study period most births occurred during the first half of May, and calving season was over by the end of May. There were always a few late births; occasionally a new calf was seen in late summer. (Subsequent to this study, calving season has extended into June as the population has increased.)

Fetal size information compiled before the study period also suggested that a large part of the calving extended over a longer period of time. Rush (1932a) reported only that there was considerable variation. E. R. Quortrup's unpublished data (Skinner 1941) indicat-

ed a size range from a 2-inch embryo to a 23-pound, 22-inch fetus; 80% of them weighed between 5 and 20 pounds when examined in late January (Appendix V).

In all Yellowstone herds during the study period, most calves were born at about the same time (early May). Observations of the earliest calves were rarely possible except in Lamar (because of limited access before 1 May), but the few records made by rangers for the Firehole suggested that first calves are usually born there perhaps a week later than in Lamar.

Calves were born on the wintering areas (Fig. 28), except for the occasional late one. In Lamar during this study, most calving took place in the lower Lamar Valley (west of Lamar Canyon in the area called the Horseshoe or Little America). Ranger reports predating the study indicated that this same area was the usual place of calving. In Pelican, most calving occurred in the eastern half of the main valley from Astringent Creek to Raven Creek. Mary Mountain animals calved in both Hayden

Fig. 28. Calves (a few days old) born about 1, May 1970, when snow was on the ground later than usual. This cow was observed deliberately pushing these calves onto their feet—an action not seen other years. Photo by Mike Sample.

and Firehole valleys. On the Firehole, most calves were born in the Lower Geyser Basin areas of Sentinel Creek, Fairy Meadows, Pocket Basin, lower Nez Perce Creek, and the Firehole Loop. Most Hayden Valley calving occurred in the western half of the big valley, near Alum Creek.

Rut

Most breeding activity occurred from mid-July to mid-August. Field observations throughout the study indicated that every year, for at least a part of that time, most of the herd groups which wintered in Lamar and Pelican intermixed in the Upper Lamar area. At the start of the rut in 1967, all of the animals were at the crest of the Absaroka Mountains on the east boundary, between the Hoodoos and Canoe Lake. In other years the groups were more scattered, some on the boundary and the adjacent ridges between Cache and Miller creeks, and some on Saddle Mountain. By the last week of July or the first week of August, some of these animals crossed the Lamar River to the Mirror Plateau, where breeding activity occurred from the meadows south of Amethyst Mountain south to the meadows at the headwaters of Pelican-Timothy-Raven creeks. Most of the breeding activity in the Mary Mountain herd occurred in the southwest corner of Hayden

Valley and adjacent forest and meadow areas. In all of these areas there were small uprooted conifers and many rubbed trees. Small wallow-sized patches of grass (Fig. 29), apparently uprooted by horning but not much used for wallowing, were another common sign of rutting activity.

The period of breeding activity observed during this study (1963-68) was shorter than that given by McHugh (1958). He observed in the much larger Hayden Valley population of that time that the season extended from 15 June to 30 September, with less activity during the first and last 2 weeks.

Movements

Migratory movements

Most of the bison in Yellowstone are migratory, moving in spring from the lower wintering valleys to higher summer ranges, and reversing this altitudinal migration in the fall. The migratory pattern was most apparent in the mixed herd groups which wintered in the Lamar, Firehole, and Pelican valleys. Although all groups of a particular wintering area did not move at once in spring, they all moved within a few days' time. Records kept during the study showed that mixed herd groups

Fig. 29. Grassy spot uprooted by bison horning during the rut.

wintering in Lamar moved 12-15 miles to higher areas of Mount Norris and the Cache-Calfee Ridge during the first week of June, 3 of 5 years, and by the last week of May twice. Firehole animals moved to Hayden Valley or the Little Firehole Meadows area of the Madison Plateau during the first week of June, 3 of 4 springs. Wintering groups began to move from lower to upper Pelican Valley at the same time. Some years, further movement across the Mirror Plateau to the Upper Lamar area was delayed until mid-June. Observations suggested that nearly every year the entire Pelican population, except some bulls, crossed to the Upper Lamar, returning to the Mirror later in the summer. Most movements took place along definite travel routes, as shown in Figs. 30 and 31.

The bulls that wintered as solitary animals, or in bull groups, left the wintering areas gradually during the spring. The last of them disappeared several weeks after the mixed herd groups moved. A few bulls were usually seen from the main roads in the Firehole, Hayden Valley, at Mary Bay, and in Lamar Valley almost to the end of June. The bulls followed not only the routes used by the mixed groups but moved upcountry along the various stream drainages to scatter widely on the summer ranges.

The cause of the spring movement was not clear. In 1966, an earlier spring than others of the study, the mixed herd groups moved from all three valleys by 24 May. In 1967, the Pelican animals were observed sequentially from the air. They moved, in 2 days, the 15 miles from the new spring growth of the upper Pelican Valley, across high meadows, which were mostly covered with snow or standing water, to the Lamar River. By the third day they were on the greening slopes of Little Saddle Mountain. They did not follow any discernible vegetation or snow melt sequence. Spring weather patterns and temperatures presumably influenced the migration. Dave Pierson (1968 pers. comm.), after years of observation, believed that warm spring days were the main factor.

In the late fall the movement of mixed herd groups was reversed, but occurred less abruptly than in the spring. Lamar animals appeared in the main valley (to stay) by late November. Some groups were reported in the Lower Geyser Basin about the middle of September most years, although the majority arrived in late October or early November. Pelican animals moved down sometime in the first 2 weeks of November, although groups commonly appeared earlier for a few days at a time when fall snowstorms occurred. This intermittent shifting from summer to winter ranges during stormy periods in the fall was also seen in Lamar.

Fig. 34. A herd group on the east boundary near Canoe Lake in early August. Photo by
John Good, Yellowstone National Park.

the Upper Lamar in 1965. In
1967, the flies were numerous in
those areas, and in Hayden Valley
also. From mid-June to mid-August 1965, neither aerial flights
nor ground checks showed mixed
herds on the Mirror Plateau, although in 1966 groups were seen
there by 24 July. From mid-June
to early August 1967, herd groups
were observed only once in Hayden Valley, but were seen, from
the air, to the south. Every year
herd groups were seldom observed in Hayden Valley during
much of July when biting insects
were at their worst.

Burger (1967a) compared biting
insect populations and animal distribution in 1966 and 1967. He
noted that the distribution and
abundance of species of *Symphoromyia,* a small gray biting fly, particularly at elevations below 8500

feet, was much greater in 1967. He
suggested that this influenced the
concentration of the entire Upper
Lamar population of bison groups
high on the east boundary, at elevations of 9500-10,000 feet, for
more than 2 weeks in late July and
early August 1967. Other summers, although the same boundary
area was used by bison, they did
not remain as long and were more
broadly distributed.

Apparently, the insect populations influenced bison distribution
and concentration more strongly
than did breeding activity. In
1966, with fewer biting flies,
mixed herd groups split and
moved from the Upper Lamar to
the Mirror while the rut was at
peak. In 1967, a similar move did
not occur until both the insect
populations and the rutting activity began to diminish.

The spring and fall migratory habits of the Yellowstone bison did not prevent animals from occasionally visiting areas of winter range during the summer. Observations made during the study period and earlier ranger reports indicated that scattered bulls sometimes appeared on all winter ranges. When population levels were higher, mixed herd groups also occasionally visited winter ranges for brief periods, according to ranger reports. Such groups were sometimes seen in the main Lamar Valley in mid-July, or more commonly, in August. Mid-summer movements of groups rarely occurred to areas near roads in the Firehole. No groups were reported near the main road through Hayden Valley in mid-summer, nor in the main Pelican Valley. No. reason for these mid-summer movements was apparent.

Winter range movements

During the winter, all bison (mixed herd groups, bull groups, and solitary bulls) moved shorter distances and less frequently than in the summer. Movement was usually confined to the limits of the wintering valleys (see Numbers and Distribution), with egress difficult if not impossible after considerable snow had fallen. Mixed herd groups moved most frequently and for greater distances, but sometimes stayed in one

locality for days or even weeks. Bull groups occupied smaller areas for longer periods. Solitary bulls sometimes spent the entire winter at one site. Presumably, the amount of movement was usually related to group food requirements. Winter conditions hindered but did not prevent occasional extensive movements by groups and single bulls between main wintering valleys. Reasons for such moves were not apparent, but forage requirements did not appear to be a factor. No movements to areas of high summer range during the winter are known; the solitary bulls wintering in these areas arrived in fall.

Mixed herd groups moved most frequently between Hayden Valley and the Firehole. In January 1965, after attempts to drive animals from Hayden Valley to the Nez Perce Creek trap with helicopters failed because of the above-average snow depths, most of the herd animals crossed of their own volition a few days later. The following winter, during the 1965-66 reduction, neckbanded animals released from the trap were seen a few days later in Hayden Valley. Before the present study, in March 1945, 54 bison traveled 6 miles across Mary Mountain in 42 inches of snow, according to McHugh (1958). The frequency of such crossings, uninfluenced by reduction operations, was unknown.

Mid-winter movements between

Lamar and Pelican valleys apparently involved only bulls. Sometime between early December 1965 and mid-January 1966, a marked young bull crossed from Lamar, presumably by way of the Mist Creek divide. Rangers reported movement on this same route by bulls in February 1932 and January 1949. Jim Stradley (1968 pers. comm.) saw a few mixed herd groups crossing from Pelican into Lamar in early winter about 1955-56.

Movements between Pelican and Hayden valleys apparently occurred in the fall and early winter, but sightings were rare. The trails of solitary bulls were followed from the air in January 1968. Mixed herd groups were reported only once during the study period east of the Yellowstone River near the Mud Volcano, but earlier reports indicated an occasional group in late fall. Jim Stradley (1968 pers. comm.) observed from the air about two dozen cows and calves moving between the two areas about 1956-57.

Movements
beyond park boundaries

Since the early years of the park, few bison have moved beyond the boundaries (Appendix VI). Figure 35 shows the locations of reported movements, which usually involved one or more bulls. Most years some bulls summered be-

yond the north boundary. Since 1951, a few bulls have been reported almost every year beyond the southwest boundary in Idaho. These movements have occurred regardless of fluctuations in population numbers.

Mixed herd groups have only been reported beyond the north boundary of the park. Late during the winters of 1943 and 1948, groups briefly left the park near Gardiner, Montana. Severe weather conditions partly influenced these moves. In summer 1943, nearly 150 bison were seen just outside the northeast corner. In the fall of 1947, 31 were 8 miles north of the boundary on Elk Creek in the Hellroaring area (R. Murphy 1970 pers. comm.). All these mixed-group movements occurred when larger numbers of bison wintered in Lamar.

Mixing of
Population Segments

Census records, aerial observations, and the limited records of neckbanded bison (Fig. 36) indicated that movements of population groups affected numbers inhabiting the winter ranges from one year to the next (population shifts), and resulted in interbreeding between populations of wintering areas during the summer. Movement occurred during the fall and winter between the valleys

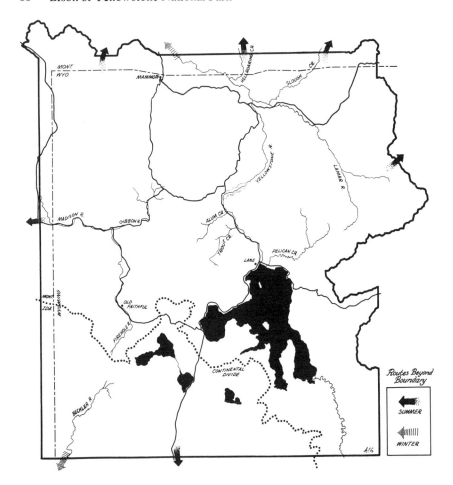

Fig. 35. Map showing known locations of bison movements across the boundaries of
   Yellowstone National Park.

of the Firehole, Hayden, Pelican, and Lamar, as previously discussed. Observations confirmed the assumption made by park personnel some years ago that the extent and frequency of mixing between the Firehole and Hayden Valley animals during most of the year, including the breeding season, justified considering them as one population, called the Mary Mountain herd, distinct but not isolated from the other two herds.

Shifts of other population groups were indicated by some fluctuations in actual winter counts from 1935 to 1950 (Fig. 37). Decreases in Lamar winter numbers

Fig. 36. Neckbanded bison in a group at Pocket Basin on the Firehole. Photo by John Douglass, Yellowstone National Park.

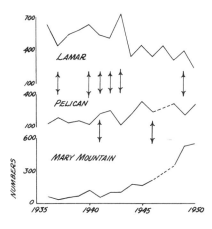

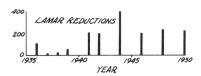

Fig. 37. Population fluctuations in wintering areas caused by shifts of mixed herd groups.

coincided with increases in Pelican in 1937, 1941, and 1942; decreases in Pelican winter numbers coincided with increases in Lamar in 1940, 1943, and 1949. Reductions, made only in Lamar during this period, probably added to the amount of decrease there in 1941 and 1942, but could not have influenced the 1937 decrease nor any Pelican decreases. Bias in Pelican population counts made by rangers on winter ski trips might account for some variation, but not the coincidence of changes in population numbers in the two valleys. Mixed herd groups which moved between Lamar and Pelican in late fall and early winter probably remained on the winter range that was in use when weather conditions worsened.

Shifts between Pelican and Hayden Valley were infrequent

and less obvious. Such shifts did occur in 1941 and 1946 (Fig. 37). Other shifts have occurred since, but the less frequent population counts made after 1950 gave no indication. During the study period, aerial observations and reduction records suggested two shifts occurred. Mary Mountain population counts after the 1964-65 reduction totaled fewer than the expected number of animals, based on numbers seen before trapping began (480), numbers removed (238), and possible natural mortality. A move of animals to Pelican after the early December count would explain the discrepancy. The next winter, in the reduction of 1965-66, 47% of the animals (yearlings and older) trapped at Nez Perce had no metal eartags, showing they had not been trapped the previous year. A movement into Hayden Valley from Pelican was the probable explanation.

Apparently, the shifts indicated in Fig. 37 were temporary, usually for the one winter. The presence of a mixed herd group (34 animals) wintering in Bechler Meadows in 1962-63 also indicated this. No herd group was reported there in 1961-62 or 1963-64. Over a span of time, the wintering numbers of the Mary Mountain, Pelican, and Lamar population segments would be unaffected by such shifts.

Observations of both total numbers of animals and individuals neckbanded in Lamar showed that, during the breeding season, intermingling of the Lamar and Pelican wintering groups was extensive most years. In 1967, all of them mixed together in several large, flexible groups at the crest of the Absarokas for more than 2 weeks. The amount of interbreeding which presumably would occur in such circumstances suggested that these bison also be considered one population segment. However, because winter season movements were so few, the separate designations were retained.

Separation was most complete between the Mary Mountain population and the Pelican-Lamar animals. The infrequent movements between Pelican and Hayden Valley at any time, coupled with the separation of the population segments during breeding season, resulted in almost no intermixing.

Historically, when there were large summering populations (parts of which wintered beyond the park area) north of the Lamar and west of the Firehole, interbreeding between the wintering populations of the Lamar and Pelican valleys, and of the Firehole and Hayden valleys, was probably less extensive because of geographic separation of some groups during the summer. Then as now, however, the groups which shared summer ranges undoubtedly interbred. Before intensive poaching greatly reduced numbers and probably altered or eliminated habitual patterns of movement, there may have been more contact between Pelican and Hayden Valley animals, but the amount of intermingling and interbreeding was probably least, even then, of the population segments.

Geographic separation during the breeding period through seasonal migration to higher summer ranges, seen in the present park bison on a local scale, could explain the existence of two recognized subspecies of bison in historic times whose distribution presumably overlapped in the Rocky Mountains (Skinner and Kaisen 1947). Possibly the mountain and plains types jointly used some wintering places along the east side of the Rockies, but breeding isolation kept the populations distinct.

The apparent temporary nature of group population shifts between main areas of winter range, discussed previously, and neckband records both suggest that animals have affinities for particular winter ranges. Neckband records for the Mary Mountain herd showed that some individuals preferred one winter valley to the other, regardless of movement between the two valleys at all seasons. The entire population (except for the many scattered bulls) had crossed to the Firehole side during the winter of 1964-65 when helicopters drove them toward the trap on Nez Perce Creek. Most summered (1965) in Hayden Valley. Those in Hayden Valley

when trapping operations again began during the winter of 1965-66 were driven across to the Firehole side to the trap on Nez Perce Creek. Aerial observations after the trapping showed that several bison, neckbanded and released, recrossed the divide to Hayden Valley immediately. During the winter of 1966-67, when there was no trapping, five marked animals (neckbanded in 1965-66) wintered in Hayden Valley: an adult cow, a 4-year-old cow, a 2-year-old cow, and two young bulls. Three marked adult cows wintered on the Firehole in both 1966-67 and 1967-68 although they were identified in Hayden Valley during summers. Less complete records on other marked cows also suggest affinity for a particular winter range although most mixed herd groups summered in Hayden Valley.

Records for the animals marked in Lamar further suggest that the tendency to winter habitually in the same valleys was stronger among mature females. Marked animals of all ages were seen on various parts of the summer range, including Raven Creek on the Mirror Plateau (close to Pelican Valley), but only three immature bulls and two immature females spent at least one winter in Pelican Valley. Cows marked as adults (five marked) were identified in winter only in the Lamar Valley, two of them for three successive winters.

A tendency for animals, particularly mature females, to prefer a given winter range might explain the lack of any lasting interchange or permanent shifts by groups from one winter range to another. The lack of emigration to new territory, such as from Pelican to Hayden Valley before the reintroduction of 1936, might also be explained. Possibly, except for young animals or old bulls, interchange between wintering valleys involved only groups. Although the basis of such groups is not known, observers generally agree that a group structure exists. Fuller (1960) believed there was a unit of some sort. McHugh (1958) believed the groups were flexible and depended little on blood relation. He did observe that cow (mixed herd) groups were usually led by mature females. These cows would then govern the movements made by the groups.

Bison have shown willingness to move considerable distances in rough topography or deep snow, according to the time of year, but they do not all intermix freely. Their movements follow repetitive patterns which indicate habit as well as physical need. The movements of both individuals and groups result in a varying amount of separation among population segments which winter in the valleys of the Firehole, Hayden, Pelican, and Lamar (Table 16). The Yellowstone bison of the present (and recent past) remain almost entirely within the park boundaries throughout the year. Those that range to the northeast (Lamar and Pelican) are almost separate from those designated the Mary Mountain herd. Affinities for given winter ranges are responsible for much of the separation, which is reinforced by migratory habits which maintain a breeding season isolation. Occasional movements by bulls and mixed herd groups prevent total separation of any one part of the population.

Food Habits

Results of analysis of 22 rumen samples, half of them collected in the winter and half throughout the rest of the year, are shown in Table 17. The 1-quart sample taken represented approximately 1% of the rumen-reticulum volume of 91 quarts averaged from eight adult males. Approximately two-thirds of the samples were taken from adult males. Because of some uncertainties in distinguishing between sedges and some grasses, doubtful material was placed in the grass category. Sedge may thus be underrepresented in the analysis.

Grasses and grasslike plants formed most of the diet throughout the year. Totals were 99, 96, 91, and 99% for winter, spring, summer, and fall, respectively. Sedge was the main source of forage at all seasons, averaging more than half the diet. Its value in win-

TABLE 16. *Comparative summary of movements shown by the present wintering populations.*

	Firehole-Hayden Valley Populations		Pelican-Lamar Populations
Winter separation	Partial	Almost complete	Almost complete
Group movement between valleys	Frequent — year around	Least frequent — fall and early winter[a]	Infrequent — fall and early winter
Seasonal migrations	Less marked		Quite marked
Summer interbreeding	Complete		Complete
Amount of movement on summer range	Range less widely (except Madison Plateau)		Range widely
Amount of movement on winter range	Varies among herd groups, bull groups, and solitary bulls		Varies among herd groups, bull groups, and solitary bulls
Movement beyond boundaries	A few bulls, SW corner		A few bulls, N&E boundaries, summer; herd groups, N boundary, winter
Summary:			
Population separation	One population: Mary Mountain	Almost separate	One breeding population, with winter range designations as Lamar and Pelican

[a]Applies to relationship between Hayden and Pelican valleys.

ter (56%) reflects the animals' frequent concentration during this season on sites where nearly all the plant growth is sedge. Grass, second in quantity during all seasons except fall, averaged more than one-third of the diet for the entire year. Its highest value (46%) in spring probably reflects both greater palatability and increased

TABLE 17. *Food habits as indicated by rumen sample analysis.*

Species	Winter 11 samples		Spring 4 samples		Summer 4 samples		Fall 3 samples		Total 22 samples	
	Freq. %	Comp. %	Freq. %	Comp. %	Freq. %	Comp. %	Freq. %	Comp. %	Freq. %	Comp. %
Grasses and grass-like plants										
plants	100	99	100	96	100	91	100	99	100	96
Sedge	100	56	100	49	100	50	100	37	100	51
Grasses	100	34	100	46	100	32	100	30	100	35
Wire rush	100	9	50	1	100	8	100	32	91	10
Spike-sedge	—	—	—	—	50	1	—	—	9	trace
Forbs	45	trace	100	3	100	6	67	trace	68	2
Phlox	18	trace	75	2	25	trace	—	—	27	1
Northwest cinquefoil	—	—	25	trace	100	6	—	—	23	1
Sulfur eriogonum	9	trace	100	trace	75	trace	33	trace	36	trace
Dandelion	73	trace	—	—	75	trace	33	trace	32	trace
Pussytoes	—	—	75	trace	—	—	—	—	14	trace
Groundsel	—	—	—	—	75	trace	—	—	14	trace
Shrubby cinquefoil	18	trace	—	—	—	—	—	—	9	trace
Clover	—	—	—	—	50	trace	—	—	9	trace
Onion	—	—	—	—	25	trace	—	—	5	trace
Blue-eyed Mary	—	—	—	—	—	—	33	trace	5	trace
Undentified	—	—	25	trace	75	trace	33	trace	23	trace

TABLE 17. (continued) *Food habits as indicated by rumen sample analysis.*

Species	Winter 11 samples		Spring 4 samples		Summer 4 samples		Fall 3 samples		Total 22 samples	
	Freq. %	Comp. %	Freq. %	Comp. %	Freq. %	Comp. %	Freq. %	Comp. %	Freq. %	Comp. %
Browse	82	1	75	trace	50	2	67	trace	73	1
Big sagebrush	36	1	50	trace	—	—	—	—	27	1
Red dogwood	45	trace	—	—	—	—	—	—	23	trace
Raspberry	9	trace	—	—	25	trace	—	—	9	trace
Dwarf huckleberry	—	—	—	—	25	2	—	—	5	trace
Serviceberry	—	—	—	—	—	—	25	trace	5	trace
Fringed sagebrush	9	trace	—	—	—	—	—	—	5	trace
Unidentified	45	trace	25	trace	—	—	67	trace	36	trace
Lodgepole pine	18	trace	75	trace	50	trace	33	trace	36	trace
Horsetail	18	trace	25	trace	25	trace	—	—	18	trace
Moss	9	trace	—	—	25	trace	33	trace	14	trace
Lichen	—	—	25	trace	—	—	—	—	5	trace
Unidentified	36	trace	75	trace	50	trace	33	trace	46	trace

Trace indicates less than 1% composition.

Material is ranked according to composition by volume, in the total diet.

Composition totals of less than 100% are the result of rounding to the nearest percent.

availability of new spring growth. Wire rush was taken yearlong, but averaged approximately one-third of the fall diet.

Both forbs and browse were represented throughout the year in the bison diet, usually as trace items. Forbs (mostly phlox) averaged 3% of the spring diet; northwest cinquefoil averaged 6% of the summer diet. Although forbs did not total a large percentage of the forage utilized, they may be an important part of the diet nutritionally.

Browse was of least importance quantitatively, forming only 1% of the year's diet. Six species were identified—four as trace values. Dwarf huckleberry represented 2% of the summer diet but occurred in only one of the four samples. Its presence may be incidental to the summer use of forested areas where it is common on the forest floor. Other browse plants shown in the analysis may also be incidental to feeding at a particular site. Their possible importance nutritionally is unknown.

Forage composition data for the bison use areas represented by the food-habits analysis are limited. Descriptions of species composition for the Lamar Valley are contained in Rush (1932b). The Soil Conservation Service (1963) and Bergstrom (1964) provide some quantitative data. Descriptions of species composition and abundance at higher elevations of the Lamar area were made by Oldemeyer (1966) and Woolf (1968). Hayden Valley species are mentioned by Kittams (1949) and the Soil Conservation Service (1964). From these sources and information obtained during this study, a list of grasses and grasslike plants was compiled according to site (Appendix VII). Forage composition information for the thermal sites used by bison during critical winter periods (see Use of Thermal Areas) has not been determined.

Wet bottomlands, creek banks, and pond edges support dense sedge growth (mainly *Carex aquatilis*, beaked sedge, and Nebraska sedge). Slightly less wet sites support a greater variety of sedges, horsetail, wire rush, and grasses such as sweetgrass, timothy (particularly in Lamar), and tufted hairgrass.

Moist meadows of the wintering valleys have some of the same sedges (*Carex acuta, C. platylepsis, C. raynoldsii*) found in the less wet sites such as swales. Smallwing sedge was the most commonly observed additonal species. Horsetail, rushes, and additional grasses, particularly bluegrass, are found. Giant wild rye is prominent in Lamar.

Moist and dry upland sites both support bluegrass species, Idaho fescue, and needlegrass. On the drier sites, junegrass and various wheatgrasses occur in most areas; the sedge *Carex xerantica* is common in Lamar.

At higher elevations on mountain herbland sites, sedges such as *Carex raynoldsii* and smallwing sedge are prominent. Rushes, bluegrasses, Idaho fescue, mountain brome, needlegrass, wheatgrass, alpine timothy, and tufted hairgrass are all common. Subalpine meadows have fewer sedges (mainly *Carex raynoldsii* and Hepburn sedge). Grasses are predominantly bluegrasses and tufted hairgrass.

8
Habitat Relationships

Use of Forage Areas

OBSERVATIONS OF BISON use of forage areas indicated preferred locations and vegetation types and suggested resulting influences on the populations. These were most apparent in winter. Forage availability did not appear to be a population-limiting factor most of the time. Conditions under which forage might be a limiting factor were suggested but not established by this study. Bison, in turn, influenced their foraging areas (see Effects on Habitat). Grasses and grasslike species which commonly occur in some forage areas are listed in Appendix VII.

During the winter, most bison concentrated on sedge sites for their forage. At Soda Butte in Lamar, 30 or more bison concentrated at times, and a few to a dozen bulls stayed all winter long. Elsewhere in Lamar, mixed herd use concentrated along Slough Creek sedge bottoms and in the many sedge swales west of the Lamar Canyon. Within the main or lower Pelican Valley, study records showed that herd use was constant, much of every year,

along the Pelican Creek bottoms where snow depths permitted. In Hayden Valley, some years, the mixed herds were seen almost all of the time along Alum Creek in the vicinity of Violet Creek. In the Lower Geyser Basin, the extensive sedge meadows of Sentinel Creek, Fairy Creek, and Fountain Flats were used most of the time by most of the animals. Use of these sedge areas was facilitated by the ability of bison to forage in deep snow (previously mentioned), and the influence of thermal activity on some of the sites (see Use of Thermal Areas).

Use of specific upland sagebrush-bunchgrass areas on the winter ranges apparently varied more from year to year. In 1965-66, on aerial observation flights, animals were observed most frequently on the north side of Pelican Creek, at the lower end of Astringent Creek, and to the west for 2 miles. The next year they were usually observed on the slopes of the southeast edge of the valley, in the vicinity of the old bridge over Pelican Creek. A third year they were in the east end of the valley. Only three times during 30 years of ranger ski patrols and once during the present study were mixed herds seen at the Mushpots-Mudkettles area of the upper valley in winter, although they crossed this area in spring. In Hayden Valley one year, the herd groups, when not on Alum Creek, ranged the north-facing slopes of the hills on the south bank of Alum Creek. Another year they were located more frequently another mile or more south, on the slopes and knobs in the southwest corner. Such differences in use of specific sites also existed on the Firehole and in Lamar. Presumably, varying patterns of snow drifting, crusting, and melting which affected forage availability influenced these shifts of use on upland sites.

During spring, summer, and fall, bison use of forage areas concentrated less on any one place or type. Use of sagebrush-bunchgrass sites increased particularly in the spring, but during all three seasons bison were more commonly seen on swales and lusher meadows where sedge species composed much of the vegetation, even at high elevations. Use of forested sites for feeding was usually limited to the more open growth and seemed incidental to other influences (rutting activity, shade needs, escape cover, travel, escape from insects). At no time did forage appear limited during these seasons, either for the present populations or for the higher populations of the past.

Observations indicated that although bison migrations between winter and summer ranges were not caused by forage conditions, less extensive movements were influenced by changes in plant growth. During the summer, with the additional influence of biting insect populations, bison moved on upward on the summer ranges as the spring season reached higher elevations. Movement among the main use areas of swales and lush spots was considerable, probably because these places were usually small in extent and widely scattered, although numerous. Local movements at all seasons appeared influenced by interspersion and size of foraging sites.

Information obtained during the present study did not indicate population levels at which severe winter conditions might limit the forage available from the complex of sedge and upland sites. Present observations were limited to relatively low population numbers and were made during mild and average winters. Observations and information from the present study and earlier did suggest that bison numbers were related to use of specific thermal sites during extreme winter conditions. Bison use of these sites may result from a combination of temporary forage limitations on the preferred sedge and upland sites, the ability of bison to reach these sites, and the direct physical influences of prolonged cold or storm conditions. Forage in these sites appeared quite limited; thus these sites may be a population regulation mechanism influencing mortality according to the numbers of bison forced to use them and the length of time they stay.

Use of Thermal Areas

Bison utilized wintering sites which were influenced by the widespread thermal activity in the park. The amount of use varied with the size of the bison group (solitary bulls, bull groups, mixed herd groups) and the kind of thermal influence. Thermal activity refers to sites where thermal features (geysers, hot springs, fumaroles) are located. The ground at these sites is usually snow-free to some extent, and streams into which the features discharge hot water may remain as ice-free travel routes for some distance from the activity. Additionally, there are places where there be no thermal features but warm ground results in small snow-free areas or larger areas where snow does not accumulate as deeply as it would without the thermal influence (Figs. 38-41).

One to several bulls used sites of thermal activity (Fig. 42) more

Fig. 38. Snow-free bison feeding site on warm ground at the edge of Fairy Meadows in the Firehole.

Fig. 39. The same site shown in Fig. 38, in early summer.

than larger bull groups and mixed herd groups did, but these sites were not used by a majority of such bulls. Scattered bulls were habitually found at various places in the Firehole, at the Mud Volcano in Hayden Valley, at Soda Butte in Lamar, and at satellite areas such as Ponuntpa Hot Springs, Violet Springs, and Mary Bay in the Pelican country. But more than half of the bulls which wintered apart from the mixed herd groups were located where there was neither thermal activity nor the influence of warm ground. Both Lamar and Hayden Valley had proportionately more of the

Fig. 40. Site along Alum Creek in Hayden Valley where warm ground causes snow to melt early.

Fig. 41. The same site shown in Fig. 40, in summer.

total number of the wintering bulls, as discussed previously. In both valleys, most of the solitary bulls and bull groups were observed apart from any site of thermal influence.

Herd groups were seldom seen at sites of thermal activity but often used areas of thermal influence, particularly sedge bottoms where snow depths were less (junction of Alum and Violet creeks in Hayden Valley (Fig. 43), Pelican Springs area of Pelican Valley, Lower Geyser Basin areas on the Firehole). They used open streams such as the Firehole River, Alum Creek, and parts of Astringent Creek (Pelican) for travel (Fig. 44), and fed on the sedge growth of the banks while in the

water (Fig. 45). Only in Lamar, of the four main wintering valleys, were thermally influenced places little used by mixed herd groups; thermal activity is least there (except Soda Butte).

Fig. 42. Bison bull wintering among active geysers and hot springs.

Fig. 43. Aerial view of the Alum Creek winter feeding area. Snow depths are less in the darker places along the creek because of warmer ground.

Fig. 44. The Firehole River is open all winter because of an influx of hot water from geysers and hot springs along the banks. Photo by Karl Bittler.

Fig. 45. Sedge growth along the banks of the Firehole River provides forage for bison and elk moving in the open water.

Total use by all bison of areas where thermal influence alleviated otherwise more severe winter conditions involved was more than the use of thermally active sites. In the Hayden, Pelican, and Firehole valleys, the amount of use of sedge bottoms with lessened snow depths, and of ice-free streams, indicated that thermal influence was important in maintaining wintering populations. In Lamar, where winters are comparatively less severe, the lack of thermal influences may not affect numbers of bison which can winter there.

Observations both before and during the study period indicated that specific sites of thermal influence where small, warm, snow-free patches occurred, sometimes

in conjunction with the activity of a few hot springs or fumaroles, were of great importance to the bison population during brief but critical periods. During the prolonged very cold spells of the severe winter of 1955-56, Jim Stradley (1968 pers. comm.) observed mixed herd groups in the scattered small, warm areas west of Astringent Creek in the Pelican area, in the Mud Volcano area of Hayden Valley, and just east of the Firehole River (Pocket Basin) in the Lower Geyser Basin (Firehole). During the study, herd groups were seen in these same Astringent Creek areas of Pelican (Fig. 46) late one winter (1968) after a stormy period and presumably were there the few other times

Fig. 46. Bison in one of the scattered small thermal areas west of Astringent Creek in the Pelican country.

Effects on Habitat

Effects on habitat as observed throughout the study period were considered from two points of view: those which seemed to occur even under low population densities of bison, and those which might have resulted from an ecological imbalance and overpopulation by bison. Bison caused or contributed to five kinds of impact on their habitat: debarking of trees, formation and maintenance of trails and wallows, trampling of sinter rock deposits in areas of thermal activity, and alteration of plant cover.

Trees which were debarked and even girdled by the rubbing and horning of bison in summer were not scattered throughout the bison use areas, but occurred in certain localities, apparently favored by both the mixed herds and the scattered bulls. In extensive areas of lodgepole pine forest on the south side of Hayden Valley (Fig. 47), in groves on the lower end of the Cache-Calfee ridge, and at a few sites on the Mirror Plateau, nearly every tree had been rubbed to some degree. Elsewhere, very small groves of trees located far from the normal summer range of the mixed herds also showed hard use, apparently by one or more of the separated bulls. Rubbing occurred during the period of shedding and regrowth of hair, when biting insects were sometimes numerous, and extended on

they could not be located in the usual places. Winters (except 1964-65) were not severe during the study period, and mixed herd groups were not observed at Mud Volcano nor in Pocket Basin. The areas were not preferred by the herd groups, since use apparently was restricted to periods of severe conditions or late winter. Forage appeared very limited in these areas and the period of use was usually very brief—a few days or perhaps a week. In spite of very limited use, these areas probably represent the margin for survival of the herd groups in Firehole, Hayden, and Pelican valleys during the most extreme winter conditions.

Fig. 47. Nearly every tree in this part of the lodgepole forest at the south edge of Hayden Valley has been debarked to some extent by rubbing bison.

through the rut. Horning of trees by bulls, more specifically associated with rutting activity, had even more effect than rubbing (Fig. 48). Although many trees survived years of this use, isolated trees and those near the edges of the forest were often killed. McHugh (1958) found that in rare cases in Hayden Valley the tree line was actually forced back, but that overall effects on reproduction were minor. Patten (1963) concluded that elk contributed to maintenance of an abrupt ecotone between forest and meadows in the Madison Range

(just west of the park) but that forest areas were increasing slowly. Similarly, the bison might impede, but not stop, the invasion of the meadow areas by the forest, which appears to be occurring.

Wallows, particularly those located in places where summering bulls commonly stayed or traveled, were used year after year. Wallows were as much a feature of these areas as were the bison themselves (Fig. 49). Even after areas such as Blacktrail Deer Creek were uninhabited by bison for a number of years, the depressions left by the

Fig. 48. Bison horning effects on a lodgepole pine.

such sites did not appear to be related to population levels; some of these places were used before the present study (Kittams 1949) and show no change in spite of greatly reduced bison numbers. Bulls were commonly seen every year and at all seasons on some of these sites, which suggested that as long as any bison inhabited Hayden Valley these favored places received heavy use. Revegetation of favored wallows might occur only without a bison population.

Trails used by bison, such as the network within Hayden Valley (Fig. 50) and those connecting main use areas such as the Mirror Plateau and Upper Lamar, were also features which appeared only indirectly related to population numbers. These routes were used historically, as now, because of habits and distribution patterns.

Areas of thermal activity used by bison, where hot pools and geysers are located, sometimes show breakage of sinter deposits by trampling. Because the rock deposits form slowly, the effects may be apparent for years. Mixed herd groups used such areas infrequently and for brief periods, according to the severity of wintering conditions, as discussed previously. Some wintering bulls used certain thermal areas throughout the winter every year regardless of changes in bison numbers.

Locations where debarked trees, wallows, trails, and trampling of thermal areas were most noticea-

wallows could still be discerned, although no differences between the vegetation within and around the depressions were apparent. When situated on slopes, wallows sometimes formed focal points of erosion, particularly in the shallow sandy soils of the hills in the southwest part of Hayden Valley. The presence and continued use of

Fig. 49. Bull bison at a wallow which is used year after year.

ble were in the Firehole-Hayden Valley part of the park. Before the present study, during the much higher bison populations of the mid-1950s, these effects caused considerable concern. The impact of the presence of bison was obvious, and may have seemed especially striking because bison (except perhaps a few strays) had been absent from that area for at least 35 years and had not been present in any numbers for at least 50 years. Then, over a span of about 15 years, the marks of bison habitation became suddenly apparent, and increased rapidly as the population expanded into this uninhabited section. The resulting concern was understandable, but perhaps exaggerated.

Observations made during the study period indicated that debarked trees, wallows, trails, and trampled thermal areas were all effects which occurred at locations favored by bison for specific activities. The amount and distribution of such effects might increase somewhat at higher population levels, but not to the same extent as the numerical increase. An assessment of such effects would not provide an indication of what a desirable bison population should be in Yellowstone.

Bison effects on plant cover were apparent on foraging areas of the winter ranges where habitat use is restricted by winter conditions. Observations indicated that effects on summer range from use by the wide-ranging bison appeared less important than influences from climatic factors (late-melting snow patches, late springs, short growing seasons) and edaphic influences (slope, soil, exposure).

During the present study, evalu-

areas of upland (usually steeper slopes and southwest exposures) in the poor and fair condition classes, producing less than 25% and 26-50%, respectively, of potential or climax vegetation. Soil erosion and disturbance (particularly in Pelican and Hayden valleys) by animal trampling and rodent activity was noted. Wetlands and subirrigated (a range classification term for some naturally occurring moist sites) lands were in good to excellent condition. The condition of these wintering valleys was attributed to use by elk and, particularly in Pelican and Hayden valleys, to winter use by bison. An evaluation of the Firehole was not made by Soil Conservation personnel, but general observations indicated that essentially the same conditions prevailed.

The effects which bison had on the vegetative cover of the winter ranges they inhabited, as the above surveys showed, were mostly confined to upland sagebrush-bunchgrass sites. Both the surveys and the present study indicated that the sedge-producing wet bottomlands and swales showed little effect. Observations made during the study indicated that bison use, particularly by mixed herd groups, occurred most frequently and for longer periods on these wet sites, which were the main source of forage. The condition of the less-used upland areas suggested that these sites were particularly vulnerable to impact and might

Fig. 50. A bison trail, one in a network connecting the most-used parts of the Hayden Valley area.

ations made of range conditions in Lamar, Pelican, and Hayden valleys by the Soil Conservation Service (1963, 1964) indicated large

remain in such condition in spite of varying patterns of use. Cole (1969) suggested that free-ranging elk would maintain upland areas in similar condition, which he termed biotic disclimaxes.

Information on the quantity and composition of the forage resources of the thermal sites used by mixed herd groups under extreme winter conditions has not been obtained. Use of these areas in stress circumstances (which occurred infrequently) rather than by preference suggests that although the forage resources appear very limited, the duration and intensity of use do not permit destruction of the vegetation.

Several considerations suggest that the effects of bison use on winter ranges, clearly apparent on upland sites, may not be greater than those which prevailed at the time the park was established. First, the habitat of the main wintering valleys (except Lamar) has been little altered by the activities of man, although animal numbers and distributions have been changed. Second, although the actual numbers of bison which originally inhabited the park area throughout the year are not known, information from this study indicated that present numbers, and those for much of the park's history, have been less than the original populations which apparently centered on the various winter ranges.

Pelican Valley may indicate the extent to which present conditions represent the past. A bison population has wintered there annually since the park was established (and probably long before), it has been least disturbed by man (reductions), and historical sources provide limited information on early habitat conditions. Jones (1875) wrote:

> This prairie is the home of great numbers of field mice and moles [pocket gophers], which have burrowed up the ground to such an extent that it is traveled over with difficulty.

The same comment could be made today, which suggests that the appearance of Pelican Valley has changed little, regardless of the cause of that appearance. If the cause (bison use) has not changed appreciably, present conditions in Pelican Valley may approximate those which prevailed at the time the park was established.

The extent to which conditions resulting from bison use of the other wintering valleys may yet resemble those of early times is less clear. In Hayden Valley, range surveys (Kittams 1949; Soil Conservation Service 1964) attributed retrogressive changes in plant cover on upland sites primarily to the effects of bison use. The absence of many bison for nearly 50 years apparently permitted a trend toward climax vegetation; subsequent repopulation caused marked retrogression which may represent reestablishment of conditions which were prevalent with use by the original bison population. Conditions resulting from use by bison in the Firehole may be comparable.

In Lamar, present effects of bison use probably represent more of a departure from early conditions. Habitat disturbance by man has been greater, bison populations were maintained in semidomestication for many years, and the area provides winter range for a more diversified ungulate population (elk; bighorn, *Ovis canadensis;* moose). The extent to which bison use and resulting effects may overlap with that of other ungulates on this range is presently being studied (William Barmore 1969 pers. comm.). Present low bison numbers contribute minimal effects on vegetative cover compared with other influences, and have much less impact than in historic times.

9
Suggested Mechanisms of Population Regulation

BISON POPULATION NUMBERS have been regulated by both natural and artificial means since the park was established. Regulation of the original bison population must have resulted entirely from environmental and populational mechanisms. Regulation, to a varying degree, has been imposed by man since near-extermination of the original bison. Limited knowledge of original bison population characteristics, habits, and distribution, together with application of ranching methods to the plains bison introduced in 1902, has influenced subsequent management practices. After 1952, all vestiges of artificial management, except reductions to control population numbers, were eliminated. Reductions were continued at irregular intervals to compensate for the alterations in natural conditions which were the accepted result of the establishment and use of the park, and settlement of the surrounding country.

Information from the present study indicates that compensatory reductions are not necessary on all population segments; the need for future reductions on any population segment is less clear. Figure 51, which shows the known Pelican Valley wintering bison population from 1902 through 1968, suggests that at least this part of the bison population has been regulated for many years without interference by man. Since the time of intensive poaching in the 1890s, reductions have been made there only twice: 118 bison in 1956, 34 bison in 1965. Following the near-extermination before 1902, the population increased gradually for nearly 20 years. Counts as shown are probably somewhat low, but suggest that a fairly stable population existed for another decade. A general slow upward trend is evident from the early 1930s to the early 1950s, but the population remained near or below 300 animals until after 1952. Between then and 1954, when 461 bison were counted, there was a marked increase. Subsequent low numbers by 1957 and thereafter seem inadequately explained by either reductions or group shifts.

110

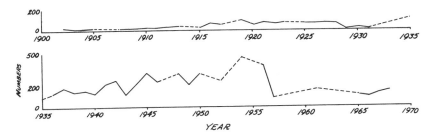

Fig. 51. Pelican Valley population numbers, 1902-68.

A complex of environmental influences probably is involved in what appears to be a naturally regulated population. Emigration from the Pelican area has not been an important factor (see Population Trends) in spite of the occasional temporary group shifts. Predation and disease, previously discussed, have been only minor influences. Environmentally influenced factors of low reproduction rates compared with those of other bison herds, low increment rates in spite of some increase in new-calf percentages following recent reductions, and heavy mortality during exceptionally severe winters appeared most important in Yellowstone as a whole. Presumably, the same factors apply to Pelican as a subunit.

Environmental effects, particularly the combination of low temperature conditions and snow depths sufficient to require considerable efforts for survival, were not measured and were difficult to observe, but were suggested by the differential mortality among sex and age classes indicated by trap records. Survival rates of calves during the first year, compared with the decreased rates among yearlings and 2-year-olds, suggested that calves, perhaps because of closer association with the cows, were not as stressed by environmental conditions. Yearlings and 2-year-olds—less closely associated with a particular adult, and of smaller size (particularly females) and less social standing compared with 3-year-olds—might be at a disadvantage, less able to forage effectively and less able to travel in deep snow. McHugh (1958) observed a dominance hierarchy based on sex and age. He noted that calves derived dominance from their cows, and that dominance was displayed in feeding situations and deep-snow travel. The stress on subordinate animals, as well as aged or otherwise weakened adults, would increase with increasingly severe weather regardless of forage availability for

TABLE 18. *Presence of factors which may affect suitability of habitat for wintering mixed herd groups.*

Valley	Bison herd groups	Sedge bottoms	Sage-Grass side hills	Warm bottomland	More than 3 thermal sites	Extensive thermal	Warm open streams	Less severe climate
Antelope Creek[a]	small	+	+					
Bechler	small	+					+	
Blacktail			+					+
Cougar Creek area[a]	small	+	+					
Elk Park		+						
Firehole	+	+	+	+	+	+	+	
Gallatin River		+	+					
Gardiner area		+	+					+
Gibbon Meadows		+						
Hayden Valley	+	+	+	+	+		+	
Lamar	+	+	+					
Norris area					+	+	+	
Pelican Valley	+	+	+		+		+	
Swan Lake area		+	+					+

[a]No bison present since mid-1950s.

the entire population. The relationship between numbers of animals, available forage, and mortality did not appear to be direct; forage quantity, although affected by snow depth and distribution, exerted effects in combination with the physical stress imposed by snow depth and storm conditions at low temperatures.

Figure 51 also shows a level below which the Pelican population has not dropped since the recovery (about 1935) from the low of 1902. Although only 88 were counted in 1957, no attempt was made to locate all animals (Jim Stradley 1968 pers. comm.). Thus, approximately 100 animals may represent the maximum population which could survive the most severe winter, but perhaps a figure of 100-200 bison better represents a level around which this population has fluctuated since 1935. That bison have survived, and at this population level, in a valley such as Pelican in spite of severe winters suggests that a margin for survival might be represented in parts of the Yellowstone environment which does not occur elsewhere.

The survival factor for bison in parts of Yellowstone may be the existence of thermal areas. As previously discussed, thermally active areas do not attract large numbers of bison for the winter, but the use of certain areas for brief periods—particularly at times of prolonged cold combined with deep snow as observed by Jim Stradley, or in late winter as seen during the study period—may determine the lower limits to which the population numbers drop.

A comparison of the larger Yellowstone valleys (Table 18) gives further evidence on which factors make habitation by bison possible. In addition to the previously discussed wintering valleys, there are other large valleys in Yellowstone where bison herd groups apparently were never known, historically or more recently. Extensive sedge bottoms are a feature of the valleys used by bison; additionally, where winter conditions are consistently less severe, as in Lamar, there are extensive open side hills of sagebrush-grassland which allow both movement and feeding. Where winters are more severe, those valleys which have bison have either extensive thermal or warm areas, or else many small ones among which movement is possible. Some streams which remain unfrozen because of an influx of warm water are an additional feature of most wintering areas, as are some river benches or valley side slopes and small hills (sagebrush-bunchgrass upland sites) which aid both foraging and movement. Where too few of these factors occur together the valleys do not now, and probably never did, support mixed herd groups of bison.

Appendix I

COMMON AND SCIENTIFIC NAMES OF PLANTS

Common name	Scientific name
Alpine Foxtail	*Alopecurus alpinus*
Alpine Fir	*Abies lasiocarpa*
Arnica	*Arnica* spp.
Balsamroot	*Balsamorrhiza sagittata*
Barley, Meadow	*Hordeum brachyantherium*
Barley, Wild	*Hordeum* spp.
Blue-eyed Mary	*Collinsia parviflora*
Bluegrass	*Poa* spp.
Bluegrass, Alpine	*P. alpina*
Bluegrass, Canby	*P. canbyi*
Bluegrass, Cusick	*P. cusickii*
Bluegrass, Kentucky	*P. pratensis*
Bluegrass, Sandberg	*P. secunda*
Bluegrass, Timberline	*P. rupicola*
Cinquefoil	*Potentilla* spp.
Cinquefoil, Northwest	*P. gracilis*
Cinquefoil, Shrubby	*P. fruticosa*
Clover	*Trifolium repens*
Dandelion	*Taraxacum* spp.
Dwarf Huckleberry	*Vaccinium scoparium*
Engelmann Spruce	*Picea engelmanni*
Eriogonum	*Eriogonum* spp.
Eriogonum, Sulfur	*E. umbellatum*
Geranium	
Giant Wild-rye	*Elymus cinereus*
Groundsel	*Senecio* spp.
Horsetail	*Equisetum* spp.
Idaho Fescue	*Festuca idahoensis*
Junegrass	*Koeleria cristata*
Lupine	*Lupinus* spp.
Mountain Brome	*Bromus marginatus*
Needle-and-Thread	*Stipa comata*
Needlegrass	*Stipa* spp.
Needlegrass, Columbia	*S. columbiana*
Needlegrass, Richardson	*S. richardsonii*
Onion	*Allium rubrum*
Phlox	*Phlox* spp.
Pine, Lodgepole	*Pinus contorta*
Pine, Whitebark	*P. albicaulis*
Pinegrass	*Calamagrostis rubescens*
Purple Onion Grass	*Melica spectabilis*
Pussytoes	*Antennaria parvifolia*
Raspberry	*Rubus* spp.

Common name	Scientific name
Red Dogwood	*Cornus stolonifera*
Rush	*Juncus* spp.
Rush, Long-styled	*J. longistylus*
Rush, Slender	*J. tenuis*
Rush, Wire	*J. balticus*
Sagebrush	*Artemisia* spp.
Sagebrush, Big	*A. tridentata*
Sagebrush, Fringed	*A. frigida*
Sedge	*Carex* spp.
	[a]*C. acuta*
	C. aperta
	C. aquatilis
	C. athrostachya
	C. nova
	C. platylepsis
	C. raynoldsii
	C. xerantica
Sedge, Beaked	*C. rostrata*
Sedge, Hepburn	*C. hepburnii*
Sedge, Nebraska	*C. nebraskensis*
Sedge, Ovalhead	*C. festivella*
Sedge, Silvertop	*C. foenea*
Sedge, Smallwing	*C. microptera*
Sedge, Valley	*C. vallicola*
Sedge, Woolly	*C. lanuginosa*
Serviceberry	*Amelanchier* spp.
Spike-sedge	*Eleocharis macrostachya*
Sweetgrass	*Hierochloe odorata*
Timber Oatgrass	*Danthonia intermedia*
Timothy	*Phleum pratense*
Timothy, Alpine	*P. alpinum*
Tufted Hairgrass	*Deschampsia caespitosa*
Western Bulrush	*Scirpus acutus*
Wheatgrass	*Agropyron* spp.
Wheatgrass, Bluebunch	*A. spicatum*
Wheatgrass, Bluestem	*A. smithii*
Wheatgrass, Slender	*A. trachycaulum*
Wheatgrass, Thickspike	*A. dasystachyum*
Willow	*Salix* spp

[a]Not listed in Booth (1950), but determined by him (1968 pers. comm.)

Appendix II

SUMMARY OF BISON REPORTS PRIOR TO 1903, YELLOWSTONE NATIONAL PARK AND VICINITY

Source	Date	Report
Raynolds (1867)	25 June 1860	crossed Low Pass from Henry's Lake to the Madison (west of Yellowstone National Park) "We have seen one band of buffalo among the hills, . . . "
DeLacy (1876)	7 Sept. 1863	eastern side of Shoshone Lake "through scrubby pines, without underbrush. There were many game trails made by the wood buffalo, whose tracks appeared numerous and fresh. We did not see any . . . "
Haines (1968 pers. comm.)	1860s	quotes local newspapers of the period as saying there was a herd of bison in the Snowy's (north of park, part of Absarokas).
Potter (1962)	1867	south end of Yankee Jim Canyon (north of Gardiner, Mont.) "That whole flat would be covered with buffalo." " 'all this buffalos',"
Cook, et al (1869)	3 October 1869	reference to Buffalo Pool, Lower Geyser Basin (Firehole area) "in one spring we saw the entire skeleton of a buffalo . . . "
Henderson (1870)	21 June 1870	Buffalo Plateau (north edge of park) "thousands of buffalo quietly grazing."
	27 June 1870	upper Buffalo Creek (north edge of park) "All game plenty—buffalo, . . . "
	2 July 1870	Lake Abundance (just beyond northeast corner of park) "Thousands of bear, elk, buffalo, and deer."
	17 July 1870	N. Fork of Clark's Fork (Broadwater River, east of northeast corner of park) "several beautiful parks, full of buffalo,..."
	22 July 1870	Cache Creek (Lamar area) "thro buffalo, elk & bear . . . all very tame."
	24 July 1870	Specimen Ridge (north edge Mirror Plateau) "Buffalo . . . "

Source	Date	Report
	8 August 1870	summit between Buffalo Cr. and Hellroaring (north edge of park) "Saw several buffalo."
	9 August 1870	head of Middle Boulder River (north of Park) "Thousands of buffalo, . . . "
Doane (1875)	18 Sept. 1870	Old Faithful (Firehole area) "numerous fresh signs of buffalo . . . "
Barlow and Heap (1872)	2 August 1871	Lower Geyser Basin (Firehole area) "Across the plain to the west . . . mud springs in ravine . . . tracks of deer, elk and buffalo . . . "
Blackmore (1872)	1872	Lamar "B.H. informs me that this valley is a favorite resort of the mountain buffalo or bison. The hills on the left were the last place that he saw the buffalo this spring followed them for nearly 30 miles and captured during his hunt 7 young calves... informs me that the M.B. congregate in bands of from 5-30 rarely more altho he has seen 50 . . . "
LeHardy (1873)	1873 (about mid-August)	"The valley of the East Fork [Lamar] extends Eastward very straight for many miles, the floor . . . deeply covered with grass. In this grass we saw in the distance quite a number of Buffalo."
Jones (1875)	1873	found bison bones embedded in soil at the bottom of a cave at Mammoth
Dunraven (1876)	1874	general locale of Yellowstone National Park. "On the little prairies, open glades, and sparsely wooded slopes, grazes the small mountain bison or buffalo, whose race has also nearly vanished from the scene; . . . "
Grinnell (1876)	1875	"The so-called 'Mountain Buffalo' was abundant in the Yellowstone Park."
Supt. Annual Report (1877)	1875	"scores if not hundreds of moose and bison were taken out of the park in the spring of 1875, . . . "

Source	Date	Report
	1877	refers to the triangle of land with the East Fork (Lamar) as the base, extending south 50 miles to the head of Yellowstone Lake (Mirror Plateau, Pelican) "Here is still a herd of three or four hundred of the curly, nearly black bison or mountain buffalo."
Holmes (1878)	1878	Twin Buttes (Firehole area) "there are some upland parks in which there are buffalo signs (the Mountain Bison)."
Raymond (1880)	1880?	"whitened skeleton of a mountain buffalo ... " (in a hot pool — Firehole area)
Supt. Annual Report (1880)	1880	"Bison or Mountain Buffalo" "Bison, so called, in the Park, are somewhat smaller, of lighter color, less curly, and with horns smaller and less spreading than those of the bison that formerly inhabited the great parks of Colorado. They have also smaller shoulder humps, and larger, darker brisket wattles. They differ materially from the buffalo of the Great Plains, being more hardy, fleet, and intelligent; their hides also are more valuable for robes, as they are darker, finer, and more curly; and these animals are, in all probability, a cross between the two varieties just mentioned. "There are about three distinct or separate herds of bison within or adjacent to the Park. [north edge of park] "The first, numbering about two hundred, pasture in summer in the valleys of the Crevice, Hellroaring, and Slough Creeks, and the mountain spurs between them, descending, with the increasing snows, to winter in the deep, sheltered grassy valleys of the East Fork [Lamar] of the Yellowstone and Soda Butte, and as the snows melt, accompanied by their young, returning to their old haunts. [Mirror Plateau and Upper Lamar] "The second, numbering over one hundred, summer in the elevated and abruptly

Source	Date	Report
		broken, little-known section of the Park, extending from the Hoodoo region to the Grand Cañon, and from Amethyst Mountain to Pelican Creek, near the foot of the Yellowstone Lake, and winter occasionally upon the East Fork [Lamar] of the Yellowstone and on Pelican Creek. Their other winter haunts are unknown. [west side of park] "The third herd, numbering about three hundred, roams in scattering bands. This season they were discovered upon the Madison Plateau and Little Madison River. Their winter haunts are unknown, though it is probable they are on the Pacific side of the Continental Divide, and, if so, they are not permanent occupants of the Park, and are therefore likely to be slaughtered by advancing settlers. "most keen of scent and difficult of approach of all mountain animals."
Yount (1880)	1880	"Here I purpose wintering [junction Soda Butte Cr.-Lamar River] so as to protect the game, especially elk and bison, in their sheltered chosen winter haunts, from the Clark's Fork and other miners."
Yount (1881)	1881	[north edge of park] "The Slough Creek and Hellroaring bands of bison did not venture near the cabin until February, nor did those of Amethyst Mountain at all; . . . I found . . . that a small band of bison wintered on Alum Creek [Hayden Valley] and another on the South Fork [Firehole River] of the Madison River; . . . "
Supt. Annual Report (1881)	1881	Mary Mountain area "It also greatly extended our knowledge of the fire holes in those regions, and afforded proof positive that a band of bison wintered there, at an elevation of nearly 9,000 feet."

Source	Date	Report
Bozeman Avant-Courier (1883)	11 Jan. 1883	"at least one band of bison, containing four hundred ... "
	22 Feb. 1883	There is a reference to the employment of hunters and meat contractors by the Park Improvement Company. refers to Lamar area "Mammoth ... Feb. 16 ... Hunting in the Park has been stopped ... parties ... contract for Eaton & Co. ... out, being unable to get the meat through from Soda Butte ... deep snow ... brought out a fine lot of buffalo meat ... hunters and meat contractors were ordered in ... in hot water."
Pierrepont (1884)	11 Sept. 1884	toward Lake Abundance from Slough Creek (north edge of park) "Five miles to the eastward they ran upon a herd of buffalos numbering about a hundred and eighty, out of which they killed seven ... "
Hague (1893)	1884	"In 1884 I estimated the buffalo in the Park at 200; ... "
Livingston Enterprise (1885)	winter 1884-85 March 7	"the herd of bison or mountain buffalo that has long inhabited the Yellowstone Mountain slopes and valleys was seen to number two or three hundred in the Park this winter."
	12 Dec. 1885	quotes New York Sun—George Bird Grinnell "There are, to my positive knowledge, not more than 700 bison ... left ... About 180 are in Yellowstone ... I have heard that twenty head were killed in Yellowstone Park by a party of English tourists."
	19 Dec. 1885	claims from a hunter "well posted" that there are 2 bands in the National Park—1 of 40 on Souce (probably Slough) Creek and 90 more or less between the forks of the Madison—supposedly some of the 40 were driven out of the park by use of explosives, and killed.

Source	Date	Report
Supt. Annual Report (1885)	1885	"The game in the Park had been shot with impunity and marketed at the hotels . . . I succeeded in a measure in breaking up the wholesale slaughter . . . . There is somewhere in the neighborhood of two hundred bison in the Park, . . . "
Supt. Annual Report (1886)	1886	"stopped the wholesale slaughter of game . . . " "From the reports . . . abundance of game [including buffalo] . . . "
Supt. Annual Report (1887)	1887	"A small number of buffalo still remain in the Park, but . . . I am unable to state their number with any . . . accuracy. My impression is that . . . they will not exceed one hundred in number. They are divided into three separate herds. One of these ranges between Hellroaring and Slough Creeks; in summer well up on these streams in the mountains, outside the Park limits, and in the winter lower down on small tributaries of the Yellowstone, within the Park. . . . this herd . . . doubtful if it now exceeds some twenty or thirty in number. . . . Another herd ranges on Specimen Mountain and the waters of Pelican Creek. . . . variously estimated at from forty to eighty. A traveler on the Cooke City road claimed to have counted fifty-four near the base of Specimen Ridge. A scouting party which I sent out during the month of May found but twenty-seven head of this herd, with four young calves . . . The third herd ranges along the continental divide and is much scattered. A band of nine or ten from this herd was seen several times this spring in the vicinity of the Upper Geyser Basin. . . . It is practically certain that none have been killed within the Park limits during the past two years, . . . "

Source	Date	Report

Supt. Annual
Report (1888)

1888

"During the early . . . winter . . . desirable . . . to secure some accurate information concerning the winter haunts of the
buffalo . . . .

"The herd of buffalo which had passed a
portion of the previous winter along
Specimen Ridge was not encountered,
and the only buffalo encountered on the
trip were three in Hayden Valley. . . .
Early in April . . . a band of buffalo were
located in Hayden Valley and along Alum
Creek. . . . a herd of buffalo numbering
at least one hundred had passed the winter
on the divide between the waters of the
Madison and Yellowstone Rivers and in
the adjacent valleys. Numbers of these
animals have been seen during the spring
along the Fire Hole River and its tributaries, and extended investigations have
shown that they range in considerable
numbers from Alum Creek, in Hayden
Valley, across the divide between the
waters of the Yellowstone and Madison
Rivers and the Continental Divide to Fall
River Basin, in the southwestern part
of the Park. From the numbers seen and
from the quantity of 'sign' observed over
an extended area, the number of these
animals that range in this portion of the
Park can be estimated at not less than two
hundred . . . . The large number of young
calves and yearlings which have been seen
leads to the belief that a natural increase is
in progress . . . .

. . .

"During the past two years, . . . but little
game has been killed . . . .

. . .

"Hunters, stimulated by the high prices
offered by taxidermists for specimens, are
now lying in wait beyond the borders of
the Park ready to pounce upon any un-
fortunate animal [ref. to bison] which
may stray beyond its limits."

Source	Date	Report
Supt. Annual Report (1889)	March 1889	"to visit the warm-spring basins on the east side of Yellowstone Lake, for the purpose of ascertaining whether or not they were the winter resorts of the buffalo. These basins, . . . well-nigh unapproachable, except when the ground is frozen and covered with deep snow, . . . successful in locating the buffalo in their haunts of the previous winter near the hot-spring basins on the divide between the waters of the Yellowstone and Madison Rivers. Although no buffalo were seen east of the Yellowstone, it was evident from the abundant signs that they habitually frequented the hot-spring basins in this locality, some of the signs being quite fresh."
Supt. Annual Report (1890)	1890	"I have no reason to believe that a single animal has been destroyed. . . . First in importance, . . . comes the buffalo. . . . enumeration . . . impossible. . . . In the summer season they are broken up into small bands and scattered over a wide area of timber-covered mountains. . . . In the winter the deep snows drive them to the open country for food. They are then found in large herds."
Supt. Annual Report (1891)	1891	"Poachers" "So long as there is no law within the Park for the prevention of hunting and trapping, it will be a most difficult matter to break them up. . . . "I am satisfied that both hunting and trapping are carried on . . . from over the western border. . . . "I learn of three or four buffalo heads that have been mounted in Bozeman, . . . I doubt not all of these were killed within the Park, or very close to the line without it. . . . fine ones are held at $400 to $1,000." . . .

Source	Date	Report
	May 1891	"I have abundant evidence, however, that the buffalo . . . are on the increase. Some tourists who went through the Park in May saw a herd of about 30, with several small calves, near the Trout Creek lunch station."
	July 1891	"In July I sent Wilson out to . . . the west line . . . found two small bands of about 30 each, one with 12 or 15 calves; in addition he saw several single ones and small bunches. I do not think it is exaggeration to say there are 200, and probably there are 400, within the Park, and that they are thriving and increasing."
Hague (1893)	winter 1891-92	"the grazing-ground in Hayden Valley was visited by a snowshoe party, who counted the scattered bands, . . . groups were generally small, and each contained a goodly number of calves. They numbered by actual count nearly 300, but there is no means of knowing what proportion of the Park buffalo were then gathered here."
Supt. Annual Report (1892)	1892	"I was informed that one Pendleton, a butcher and poacher from Cooke City, had captured two buffalo calves on specimen range, and had taken them across the north end of the Park, . . . "there are certainly not less than four hundred here; of these about 20 percent were calves last year. This year, also, the calves seem numerous and prosperous. The great value placed upon them by sportsmen and taxidermists makes their protection difficult, . . . "

Source	Date	Report
Hague (1893)	1893	"That buffalo were among the animals inhabiting the Yellowstone Park was known in the early days of its history; ... The Park buffalo may all be classed under the head of mountain buffalo, and even in this elevated region they live for the greater part of the year in the timber. ... their habits are quite different from ... the buffalo of the plain, and it is most unusual, save in midwinter, to find them in open valley or on the treeless mountain slope. They haunt the most inaccessible and out-of-the-way places, ... living in open glades and pastures, the oases of the dense forest, often only to be reached by climbing over a tangle of fallen timber .... the rapidity of their disappearance on being alarmed . ... It is surprising how few buffalo have been seen in midsummer, even by those most familiar with their haunts and habits. They wander about in small bands in such unfrequented country as the southern end of the Madison plateau, the Mirror plateau, and the head of Pelican Creek, and on the borders of that elevated tableland known as Elephant Back. In winter, leaving the forest, they feed over the slopes of Specimen Ridge, and in the open Hayden Valley. "It is not likely that there ever were many buffalo in the Park, ... If they ever roamed over this country in large herds, evidence of the fact should be apparent by well-trodden buffalo trails, which nowhere form a feature of the Park plateau. ... They occasionally wander beyond the Park Borders into Idaho and Montana with the first fall of snow, returning to their mountain homes with the approach of spring."

Source	Date	Report

Supt. Annual Report (1893) — 1893

"As the game diminishes in the adjacent States, professional hunters and trappers become more bold and more active. Montana, Idaho, and Wyoming all have stringent game laws, but in spite of them the game grows rapaidly less. . . . A stringent law, with severe penalties, is one of the most urgent needs of the Park. . . . Confiscation of the outfit, under existing regulations, has but little effect, as the outfit is generally worthless. "I have pretty reliable information that about a dozen buffalo were killed last winter, and it is not improbable that even more shared that fate. The heads of these were mounted . . . .

"The buffalo have been seen often during the year, and they appear to be doing well. In all the herds a fair proportion of calves is found. Those killed have been mostly bulls, so the capacity of the herd for increase has not been diminished. Late in June a herd of fifty to sixty crossed the road from west to east near the Riverside Geyser. Thirteen calves were counted. They were . . . very tame, and not the least scared by the soldiers who went among them. The estimate of four hundred placed on their number last year is surely not too high."

Hough (1894) — spring 1894

"We counted 75 to 85 head of buffalo in Hayden this trip. . . . Sergt. Parker makes the Hayden and Nez Perce district buffalo 81 head. Capt. Scott counted 103 head in Hayden Valley one day three weeks ago. One band of 6 and another of 7 head were seen in the Pelican country, . . . We saw three head in Nez Perce Valley."

Hough states that Howell was killing cows and calves, and probably killed, during the winter, more than the 11 known killed at his capture in March, as he had been in Pelican since September. Also Hough states 19 were killed SW of the Park by Indians, fall '93; that 7 other

Source	Date	Report
		heads were offered to a Bozeman taxidermist; that 6 or 8 dead bison were found in Hayden Valley, "John Folsom discovered ten head more of dead buffalo in that same part of the country;" and that "I have track of several other heads." "I think forty buffalo have been killed this fall and winter, and no one knows how many more."
		"The buffalo do sometimes cross the divide about where we did, and work between the hot country of Mary's Mountain and this sheltered little valley. They have not wintered on the west side of the divide in any numbers for a considerable time.
		"wild wall of mountains which we saw to the north of the Yellowstone—so desolate and forbidding that even now . . . . there may be a few head of bison left over beyond the Bison Peak — . . . .
		"I do not personally believe there are over 150 buffalo left alive in the Park."
Supt. Annual Report (1894)	1894	"not able to report any diminution of poaching . . . " (describes Howell poaching case, with Howell caught killing 5 bison in Pelican, and his cache of 6 additional heads).
		"The dead bodies of 13 bison have been discovered in their winter range. . . . convinced they perished from natural causes."
		"Buffalo have been more carefully watched and more accurately counted than ever before. After deducting the losses from all causes, I feel disposed to reduce my estimate . . . to 200, . . . A few were seen in their winter range as late as the middle of June, and these had calves with them."

NOTE: Garretson (1938) states that during the winter of 1893-94 most of the buffalo were on the Madison Plateau, that 76 head were killed on the west side, and 40 head in the Gallatin valley. He states that no more than 20 could be counted thereafter. He cites no source for his statements, and while the poaching was undoubtedly heavy that year, neither the losses nor the population figure afterwards were stated as fact by any of the recorders of the time.

Source	Date	Report
Marble (1932)	no date	mentions Dick Rock (of Henry's Lake, west of the park) catching 5 calves.
Murri (1968)	no date	reference to Dick Rock getting his buffalo calves in the Bechler Meadows in early spring, known to have gotten a pair.
Hofer (1927)	approx. 1894 or 1895	"Hunters from the West Side were getting calves in the early spring and heads in the winter. From near Gardiner three young fellows killed a number in the basin. These were the ones we found when I was with E. Hough . . . " (some of those presumed dead of natural causes).
Supt. Annual Report (1895)	1895	"The act of May 7, 1894, seems to have had . . . effect upon the poachers . . . those of the north, the east, and the south sides have nearly . . . ceased . . . . I can not say as much for the Idaho border. . . . So long as the only herd of wild bison now existing in the United States is on the border of this State, . . . inquiry into various rumors of the killing of bison, either in the Park near the Idaho line or across it . . . convinced me that this last remaining herd is in danger of extinction by these people. . . . I have good evidence of the killing of at least ten less than two years ago . . . prior to the passage of the protection act, . . . I have undoubted evidence of the capture of three calves this spring by a resident of Henry's Lake. . . . There are rumors of a herd of nearly one hundred having been seen in Idaho outside the Park within the last two or three months. [Comments that there was less snow than before known, that the large game could pass at will.] "the bison that have heretofore wintered in the Hayden Valley were not massed there this year. The most seen there in a single bunch . . . was about thirty. Small herds of from three to four to ten were seen in widely separated localities

Source	Date	Report
		where they have not usually wintered. I feel sure that many of them did not leave their summer range along the Idaho line. [undetermined losses] . . . but I fear that their number has not increased, . . . estimate . . . two hundred still remain."
Supt. Annual Report (1896)	1896	"I . . . organized three parties for operations against the merciless freebooters of the Henry's Lake country. . . . The ground covered by the buffalo in their summer range was most thoroughly gone over. Carcasses, . . . of about ten buffaloes were found, . . . One party of poachers was encountered, . . . I obtained information . . . buffalo scalps for sale in the city of Butte. "For some reason the main herd did not winter in Hayden Valley as usual, and on the extensive scouts made by my order during the winter months only about a dozen in all were seen. They were scattered singly and in small bunches over a large portion of the Park. Within the last month [July] one party reported a small bunch of 3 in one place, and of 12 in another. A second party reported a bunch of 3 in a valley in a distant part of the park, and tracks of a herd of 8 or 9 more, but this herd was not seen. From reports received, I feel confident that the majority wintered in the extreme southwest corner of park, in the Falls River [Bechler] meadows; and I also feel sure that there are now a considerable number east of the Yellowstone River. . . . fair certainty of the existence of 25 or 30, and possibly of 50."
Snake River Monthly report	21 Aug. 1897	"By way of Summit Lake. Saw sign of about 20 buffalo . . . " (Madison Plateau)
Whittaker (1897-99)	14 Nov. 1897	sign of 5, Mary Mountain area (Hayden Valley)
	18 Nov. 1897	sign of 2, Astringent Creek (Pelican Valley)

Source	Date	Report
Supt. Annual Report (1897)	1897	"game, buffalo excepted, is increasing. "The number of buffalo is estimated at 24. "the buffalo remaining in the park are now scattered in very small herds at a number of points far remote from each other. They are mostly in rough rugged regions, ... "But very few buffalo have been reported this season. The scouts, however, seldom see much sign in the summer, and now the few remaining buffalo are scattered and range in the most remote and inaccessible parts of the park in summer. I am confident of finding 25 this winter, when the snowshoe season sets in, and hope there are nearly double this number in the park. Since Idaho has forbidden the killing of buffalo . . . I have strong hopes . . . protect them from further slaughter by poachers." The section containing instructions to stations recognizes known buffalo haunts as: Mirror and Lamar, Hayden Valley, and the Firehole area.
Soda Butte Station Record	19 Feb. 1898	reports wild buffalo
Morrison (1897-98)	Feb. 1898	refers to Mirror Plateau "across to Broad Cr up it to hot springs near Fern Lake . . . Ponuntpa Springs to look for buffalo. Found numerous signs of buffalo all around the spring and on both sides of Sour Cr. after followed them down Sour Cr. to where a hot creek came down from a hot mountain on the north which they went up, and a close examination of the trail . . . [the trail was not made in single file but band was spread out] I estimate the band as follows 4 calfs, 8 bulls, about 8 to 9 cows, but think some of the signs which I took for cow signs may have been 2 yr. old bulls. In all 21 head. Ponuntpa Springs is an ideal wintering place for the band which is there as there is no snow

Source	Date	Report
		to speak of on the flat which is about a mile long and 3/4 wide and is covered with hot springs and hot creeks . . . "
	11 April 1898	sign, estimate of 3, 4 miles north of the Upper Basin, Firehole area
Lake Station Record	21 June 1898	old sign—hot formations on Mary Mt.
Morrison (1897-98)	July 1898	"head of Pelican Cr went west to a small creek that flows in to Broad Cr . . . down Broad Cr about 2 miles thence NE. to hot springs on Shallow Cr up Shallow Cr to Wapiti Lake thence east to camp. Saw signs of 3 buffalo fresh 2 on the small creek that flows into Broad creek and one at Wapiti Lake."
	7 July 1898	"left . . . head of Pelican Cr went down it 5 miles made camp . . . went over to Fern Lake around it to head of Sour Cr down it then followed buffalo trail fresh over ridge to Broad Cr, up it to Fern Lake and on to Tern Lake . . . to camp. Saw one buffalo jumped 5 buffalo near ford of Broad Cr followed them to Fern Lake where we saw the one was on one of the heads of Sour Cr. an old bull. Around Ponuntpa Springs there were fresh signs of the band I saw there last winter."
	8 July 1898	5-6 buffalo wintered near forks of Pelican Cr., fresh signs
Lake Station Record	27 July 1898	one bull buffalo on top of Mary Mt.
	14 Aug. 1898	buffalo signs near headwaters of Raven Cr. (Pelican area) supposed to have been made within the last 20 days—quite a bunch of buffalo hair was found at outlet of White Lake
Morrison (1897-98)	12 Sept. 1898	signs 1 bull 6 mi from W boundary
	13 Sept. 1898	West Boundary headed for Summit Lake "3 m. east of bound. near a little spring saw where 5 buffalo had bedded over night. probably 2 bull a yearling and 2 cows."

Source	Date	Report
Whittaker (1897-99)	30 Sept. 1898	a trip was made up the Lamar to Cold Cr. and Mist Cr., over the divide to the head of Willow Cr. (Mirror Plateau area) and down Raven Cr., up to Pelican, to Broad Cr. and return to Pelican "will make special report on buffalo"
Morrison (1897-98)	10 Oct. 1898	Mirror Plateau area "fresh trail of 2 buffalo at head of Willow Cr. they came down Mist Cr. to the mouth . . . evidently a cow and a yearling from the tracks . . . "
Whittaker (1897-99)	12 Oct. 1898	refers to Mirror Plateau area "but after riding around the entire summer range i could not find any sign of them met Scout Morrison . . . presume they have all left their summer range on Flint and moved to either the head of Pelican Creek or Willow Creek where i saw some sign of them on my last trip . . ." (see date of 30 September 1898)
Burgess (1898-99)	18 Oct. 1898 19 Oct. 1898	Bechler area one, track "went to [Bechler] River saw 2 year old buffalo tracks . . ." "tracks of about 6 B They had been made 6 or 7 days ago."
	20 Oct. 1898	Firehold to Fountain "saw the Buffalos had been going along the river to the L[one] Star Geyser."
	10 Nov. 1898	Trout Cr. to head of Nez Perce Cr. "I found two Buffalo tracks one Bull and cow"
	13 Nov. 1898	"Then to East Fork of Pellican, where I saw the tracks of one buffalo."
	23 Nov. 1898	east side of Hayden Valley "Went East to Forest Springs. found old signs of Buffallos . . . to worm formation at head of Moss Creek. found some fresh Buffallo tracks going South . . . and down in sour creek where there is quite an opening there I found where 4 Buffalos had beded the night before. from there I went to . . . Cotton grass and Sour Creek I saw 2 old Bulls one laying down they were very wild, and ran back toward sour creek."

Source	Date	Report
Supt. Annual Report (1898)	1898	estimates 50 yet in the park "This is about the only wild herd in the United States, and steps should be taken to prevent the extermination of this herd from the evils of inbreeding . . ."
Burgess (1898-99)	10 Jan. 1899	refers to Mirror Plateau area "up East forks of Estringent [Astringent Creek] to Head of Bluff Creek. Then to White Lake. I saw two Buffalos and a Great Many tracks. then went to Tern Lakes on the East side of the lake saw four Buffalos Then we went to Fern Lake. Saw 3 Buffaloes on the northwest End of Lake."
	11 Jan. 1899	"went up middle Estringent, over White Lake to head of Sour Creek, on this Creek I saw 15 Buffalos 12 old one and 3 calfs. went down sour creek . . . .. On this same trip, no sign was found in Hayden Valley.
	6 March 1899	". . . 2 Buffalo . . . wintering on snake river."
	9 April 1899	"went to Estringent Cabin"
	10 April 1899	"I looked for the Buffalos. saw 20"
	14 April 1899	"went to Trout Creek one buffalo on Crater Hill"
	15 April 1899	"went to Fountain 5 Buffalos on Central Plateau"
Whittaker (1897-99)	12 May 1899	"saw one Buffalo near the Base of Hell-Roaring Mountain about a 4 year old . . ."
Lake Station Record	1 June 1899	buffalo sign at Mary Mt.
Whittaker (1897-99)	15 Aug. 1899	"to the headwaters of Deep Creek and flint creek on the mirror plateau to look for the Buffalo. could not see any but found numerous sign . . ."

Source	Date	Report
Holt (1899-1901)	23 Sept. 1899	Snake River to Lake "fresh signs of two buffalo . . ."
	8 Oct. 1899	"Buffalo passed within sight of camp . . ." (Thorofare area)
	26 Nov. 1899	Ponuntpa area, Mirror Plateau "no fresh signs of Buffalo. found skeleton of calf."
Supt. Annual Report (1899)	1899	"it is not known how many there are left or whether or not they are in- creasing. I shall try and find out this winter as to their number. One of the scouts saw twenty-six last spring, and signs were seen of others. It is probable that there are fifty or more."
Supt. Annual Report (1900)	1900	"Twenty-nine head of buffalo were counted by scouts last winter, and there were possibly 10 more in the park that were not seen. Unless stations are located near the two southern corners of the reservation and the force of scouts increased the buffalo will be exterminated in a few years. With that addition to the facilities for protection they can be pre- served and will increase."
Supt. Annual Report (1901)	1901	"it has been impossible . . . to ascertain accurately the number of buffalo . . . but . . . as soon as the snow falls, . . . The buffalo are now protected by the laws of Wyoming, Idaho, and Montana, and it is now possible that the small herd remaining in the park may increase, though it may be necessary to introduce some new blood in this herd, and pos- sibly it may be well to start an entirely new one and to keep it under fence, turning the animals loose gradually as the herd increases. From what I can hear I do not believe that there are more than 25 buffalo left in the park." (One bull was killed in Jackson Hole.)
Lake Station Record	8 Dec 1902	patrolled to Pelican Country, 1 buffalo

Source	Date	Report
Supt. Annual Report (1902)	1902	"In addition to the large corral that has been constructed near the Mammoth Hot Springs, a small corral . . . on Pelican . . . to capture therein the few remaining buffalo . . . During the past winter . . . 22 of these animals on the head of Pelican Creek, and there are probably a few more that we were unable to find. This herd is exceedingly wild, and will probably never increase in size, and may possibly die out completely. It is thought that we can catch up some of the young. . . . . . . "It is our intention to feed and handle the new herd of buffalo in the same manner as domestic cattle. . . ."

Appendix III

REPORTS OF WILD BISON 1903-19, YELLOWSTONE NATIONAL PARK.

Source	Date	Report
Lake Station Record	19 Jan. 1903	returned from Pelican 15 buffalo
	15 Feb. 1903	Pelican country 1 buffalo (main valley)
	26 Feb. 1903	from Pelican 19 buffalo
	24 Mar. 1903	from Pelican seen 17 buffalo
	25 Mar. 1903	Pelican 19 buffalo
	12 May 1903	"from Pelican Country . . . Had 2 Buffalo bull calves on toboggan drawn by dogs. Saw 16 old buffalo and 3 calves."
Supt. Annual Report (1903)	spring 1903	2 calves captured from wild herd
Lake Station Record	4 April 1904	located one buffalo at the hay stack (Pelican)
	end April	Scouts—Pelican Valley—"seeing 11 Buffalo 5 cows and 6 bulls no calves saw 6 dead ones"
Superintendent's Journal, 1903-21	6 May 1904	party that went out for buffalo calves report finding as follows . . . 11 live buffalo 5 dead buffalo—4 old ones and 1 yearling (additional report of one old bull dead between Lake and Thumb refers to one of the three Goodnight bulls which was turned out)
	18 May 1904	party returns, having captured one female calf on the head of Sour Creek; they saw twelve live buffalo; men at Canyon station saw two in Hayden Valley
Supt. Annual Report (1904)	spring 1904	remnant located on the head of Pelican Creek. "three calves have been caught up from the wild herd . . . Two of these are males and one is a female." (the two males were those caught the previous year)
Supt. Annual Report (1905)	1905	"now about 30 of these animals left, . . . on the head of Pelican Creek."
Supt. Annual Report (1907)	probably summer	sign of 15, Mirror Plateau and Specimen Ridge; signs of 6, Madison Plateau.

Source	Date	Report
	Aug. 1907	4 seen in Hayden Valley total estimated to be 25
Scout Monthly Reports (1908)	1 April 1908	2 bull buffalo, Pelican Valley (near Raven Creek)
	13 April 1908	followed buffalo trail up Lamar to mouth of Mist Creek, saw 10 buffalo, 2 of them yearling calves
	16 April 1908	sign as far down the Lamar as Miller Creek where buffalo had been feeding.
	13 July 1908	9 including 1 calf on upper Lamar
	7 Sept. 1908 (approx.)	"Patrolled west to Buffalo Lake, then south to 10 miles . . . saw . . . signs of buffalo" (southwest boundary)
	16 Sept. 1908	patrolled northeast to Mist Creek and camped. 18 miles Saw 20 wild buffalo (apparently at the Mushpot-Mudkettle area on Pelican Creek)
	9 Oct. 1908	11 seen (on trip through Willow-Mist-Upper Pelican Creeks of the Mirror Plateau)
	11 Oct. 1908	saw 7 head buffalo at Pelican Bridge (this report, as well as later ones for the immediate vicinity of Lake may refer to the Yellowstone Boat Co. animals)
Supt. Annual Report (1908)	1908	"Wild herd: Reports from scouts and patrols state that signs of two buffalo calves were seen on Mirror Plateau and one cow and calf were seen in Pelican Valley during the season. Scout Wilson reported that he saw 10 buffalo at the mouth of Mist Creek on Lamar River on April 13. On September 7 Scout McBride saw fresh tracks of 2 buffalo on Boundary Creek, near the western boundary, and on September 16 he saw 20 buffalo near the mush pots southwest of Pelican Cone in the valley of Pelican Creek. From these reports it is evident that the remnant of the original wild herd is gradually increasing in numbers."

Source	Date	Report

| Skinner and Alcorn (1942-51) | 1908 | used a figure of 32 counted. |

NOTE: On October 15, 1907, the Yellowstone Lake Boat Co. E. C. Waters corrals at Lake were torn down and the 8 buffalo within released. The Lake Station Record for the next two years and the scout diaries indicate that the various sightings of buffalo west of Lake Station, between Lake Station and Mud Geyser, and from Lake to Pelican Creek Bridge and east along the lakeshore for several miles were probably these animals. Reports of animals seen, or sign thereof, for these areas in 1908-09 are not included as part of this summary. Four or five buffalo were rounded up at Lake to be driven to headquarters in early December of 1909. North of Canyon, with average snow depths of 4 feet, the buffalo broke away. When last reported they had gone down into the Yellowstone Canyon to feed, apparently in the vicinity of Seven Mile Hole, where survival would be unlikely. Probably any left near Lake disappeared one by one without ever mingling with the wild herd. There was no indication that they ever joined the tame herd, of which very close track was kept at this time. The Boat Co. animals were of Goodnight plains bison stock, brought to the park in 1896, and kept in corrals (Timmons 1962).

Lake Station Record	15 & 16 Jan. 1909	patrol to Astringent Creek and White Lake, buffalo sign seen
	23 March 1909	patrol to Astringent Creek cabin and White Lake, 3 buffalo seen
	24 March 1909	sign at the Mushpot area on Pelican Creek
Scout Monthly Reports (1909)	15 April 1909	4 buffalo near Yellowstone Lake, very thin (these may have been part of Boat Co. animals, 6 were driven across the Pelican Bridge in Nov. 1908)
	16 April 1909	Astringent Creek to Mist Creek and Lamar and to Willow Creek cabin, saw 3 buffalo near cabin
	17 April 1909	patrolled north to Soda Butte, saw 2 buffalo
Supt. Annual Report (1909)	April 1909	"Another small herd of 9 was seen near Pelican Creek in April." (this may be an error, representing the total of the above-listed trip)
Scout Monthly Reports (1909)	mid-May 1909	"trying to corral 9 wild buffalo near Cache Cr. We captured 1 buffalo bull calf"

Source	Date	Report
Supt. Annual Reports (1909)	May 1909	"A herd of 11 wild buffalo was seen on Cache Creek May 19, at which time a bull calf was caught . . . "
Anonymous File No. 21 & 22, 5/28/09	15 May 1909	lists 10 at the mouth of Cache Creek—2 large bulls, 7 cows, 1 calf
Supt. Annual Report (1909)	July 1909	"Signs were also seen in the southwestern part of the park in July of this year."
Lake Station Record	23 Dec. 1909	Buffalo signs seen at Squaw Lake (Pelican area), 23 buffalo seen near Pelican Springs
	13 Jan. 1910	buffalo signs 2 mi. west of Steamboat Sp. (Yellowstone Lake, north edge)
Scout Monthly Reports (1910)	February 1910	Soda Butte to Cache Creek and return, saw 5 buffalo and signs of buffalo.
Anonymous File No. 21 & 22, 3/2/10	23 Feb. 1910	29 buffalo seen on Pelican Creek (states group known not to contain the Boat Co. buffalo)
Supt. Annual Report (1910)	1910	"A herd of 29 wild buffalo was seen in Pelican Valley on February 23, and a small herd of 5 was seen on Cache Creek on February 3. One old bull died during the winter in the vicinity of Yellowstone Lake, . . . " (the one may have been from the Boat Co.)
Lake Station Record	9 March 1910	(Pelican Valley) "seen 20 of them"
	16 March 1910	from Park Point (Yellowstone Lake) to Pelican Creek, 6 buffalo
	17 March 1910	from Astringent Cabin to Lake, 21 buffalo
	30 June 1910	Lake Station to 14 mile post, Sylvan Pass Rd., saw 7 buffalo
Lake Station Record	17 Feb. 1911	patrol to Pelican Cr., 20 buffalo
Anonymous File No. 21 & 22, 3/14/11	Feb. ?	part of wild herd sighted recently, sure of 20, think 25 including some calves

Source	Date	Report
Lake Station Record	2 March 1911	to Pelican Cabin, 25 buffalo
Scout Monthly Reports (1911)	28-30 April 1911	from Signal Point (on Yellowstone Lake) north to Astringent Creek, saw 27 wild buffalo of which 2 were calves, traveled to Mist, Cold, and Willow Creek cabin N. to Lamar River, "sign of one wild buffalo"

NOTE: During June 1911, 4 bison were rounded up on the Madison and brought to Mammoth, in the mistaken belief that they were Yellowstone National Park animals. They were returned, including offspring, to their owners (Sherman) at Henry's Lake in June 1913 (Scout Reports and File No. 21 & 22).

Nowlin (1912)	1911	comments droppings indicated buffaloes had ranged near Saddle Mountain and on Mist Creek and the upper Lamar River; plenty of old signs along Pelican Creek, at White Lake on the head of Sour Cr., and near the heads of Deep Creek.
Thumb Station Record	10 August 1911	"patrolled to K. W. & De L. C. Reg. 82– 8 buffalo" (contrary to the Supt. Report, 1911, the 8 buffalo were probably seen at the Knotted Woods, southwest of Dryad Lake, rather than west of Thumb at DeLacy Creek)
Supt. Annual Report (1911)	1911	"The wild herd has been seen several times, usually in the Pelican Creek Valley. The largest number seen at any one time was 27. A patrol reported having seen 8 along the road, about 7 miles west of Thumb Station, on August 12." (error, see above)
Anonymous File No. 21 & 22 5/3/12 7/19/12	13 July 1912	48 (inc. 10 calves) on Raven Creek "Scouts McBride and Little . . . report having actually seen and counted 48 animals. They are not together in a herd, but are considerably scattered, mostly on Pelican Creek, Upper Lamar River and tributaries." count included 10 this year's calves; one additional large bull on the Pitchstone for a total of 49

Source	Date	Report
Scout Monthly Reports (1912)	6 July 1912	1 bull, signs of 1 more, Cache Cr. (may have been from tame herd)
	7 July 1912	sign of a small band, between Cache and Willow Creek
	8 July 1912	sign of 6, Willow Cr. (seen by another scout)
	9 July 1912	fresh sign, vicinity of Mist Cr.
	10 July 1912	1 bull, signs of others, Mist Creek.
	11 July 1912	fresh sign, Mist to Raven Creek. (one seen by another scout)
	12 July 1912	"patrolled county" (Mirror Plateau), saw 38: 25 cows, 3 bulls, 10 spring calves, one seen between Snake River and Aster Creek
	22 July 1912	saw buffalo signs on Proposition Creek.
Nowlin (1912)	22-30 July 1912	trip made on Specimen Ridge and Mirror Plateau, upper Lamar River, Saddle Mt., Miller and Cache Creeks; fresh sign cow & calf Upper Pelican, tracks and droppings at head of Raven Creek, about 10 days old
		saw about 10 at the head of Timothy Cr., followed them to the headwaters of Clover Creek where they joined others, "all were feeding quietly in an open park."
		total of 35: 7 bulls inc. 2 large ones, 13 cows, 7 yearlings, 8 young calves, fresh sign of two bulls on Timothy Creek
		total counted for trip: 39
		"However, the summer range is so extensive and difficult to traverse that it would require a great deal of time and careful work to examine it thoroughly. ... I have never seen buffaloes on the range so wary and difficult to locate as the wild ones in the Yellowstone Park. ... As these buffalo winter around the warm springs ... it seems reasonable to me that if undisturbed, they ought to gradually increase."
Scout Monthly Reports (1912)	20 Sept. 1912 (approx.)	2 buffalo seen between Cold Creek and the Lamar R.
	27 Sept. 1912	25 wild buffalo, vicinity of Saddle Mt.

Source	Date	Report
Supt. Annual Report (1912)	1912	"A special effort was made during the month of July to determine as nearly as possible the exact number of buffalo in the wild herd in the park. Forty-nine animals, including 10 this year's calves, were counted. ... indicates that the herd is thriving beyond expectation."
Anonymous File No. 21 & 22 8/2/12	winter 1912-13	added note: "Men on Lake Station claim 53 winter 1912-13 but not officially reported."
Scout Monthly Reports (1913)	28 Feb. 1913 March (early)	saw 35 wild buffalo, trip from Yellowstone Lake outlet to Pelican cabin 1 bull, head of Mist Creek
Lake Station Record	17 March 1913	53 buffalo, patrol from Pelican cabin
Scout Monthly Reports (1913)	April	1 bull, trip from Cache to Willow Creek on top of Miller Creek divide
Lake Station Record	30 May 1913	2 buffalo, patrol to Cub Creek
Scout Monthly Reports (1913)	5 Sept. 1913	20 buffalo, trip from Cold Creek to Frost Lake
Supt. Annual Report (1913)	1913	"No accurate count of the wild herd of buffalo was made, but scattering bands of them have been seen, and one party on patrol reports having seen 7 calves with a herd at a distance. It is believed that there has been some increase."
Scout Monthly Reports (1914)	September	sign seen, vicinity of Saddle Mt.
Supt. Annual Report (1914)	1914	"No particular effort was made to make an accurate count ... but they have been seen in considerable numbers on several occasions, ... increasing slowly."
Stevenson (1915-16)	4 Dec. 1915	"went up Pelican Creek and Raven Creek to count Buffalo. 4 found on Pelican Cr. 27 on Raven Cr 31 in all about 5 large bulls 6 yearlings 4 calves and the rest cows and young bulls."

Source	Date	Report
Supt. Annual Report (1915)	1915	"has not been practicable to get an accurate count . . . "

NOTE: Superintendents' Annual Reports for a few more years indicate wild herd numbers, which will not be included in this summary, as they may represent the addition of some escaped tame-herd members.

144

Appendix IV

BISON POPULATION 1902-68.

Winter	Lamar			Pelican			Mary Mountain			Total		
	Actual Ct.	Loss	Est.	Actual Ct.	Loss	Est.	Actual Ct.	Loss	Est.	Actual Ct.	Loss	Est.
1901-02	21			23		25				44		46
03	28	1		19						47	1	
04	39	2		12	5					51	7	
05	44			30		30				74		
06	57											
07	59	2		15		15	10		10	84	2	
08	73	1		20			2			95	1	
09	95	5		23						118	5	
10	120	3		29						149	3	
11	141	2		27						168	2	
12	143	28		48			1			192	28	
13	162	8		53						215	8	
14	193	5										
15	239	4		31						270	4	
16	276	18		72						348	18	
17	330	8		67	3					397	i1	
18	385	5										

19	414	45		90	1				504	46	
20	440	17		61					501	17	
21	526	7		76					602	7	
22	578	56		69					647	56	
23	672	14		76					748	14	
24	753	13									
25	764	109		66					830	109	
26	866	23		65					931	23	
27	936	41		72					1008	41	
28	996	54		61	4				1057	58	
29	1092	106		17					1109	106	
30	1097	132		27					1124	132	
31	1182	120		10					1192	120	
32	1016	222									
33	985	207	1000								
34	950	177									
35	830	264	1000								
36	640	109	708	136		150	71		847	109	929
37	456	17	488	188		200	30	68	674	17	756
38	554	25	577	146		160	55	63	755	25	800
39	582	67	605	157		165	72	80	811	67	850
40	630	3	675	122		165	116	130	868	3	970

Winter	Lamar Actual Ct.	Lamar Loss	Lamar Est.	Pelican Actual Ct.	Pelican Loss	Pelican Est.	Mary Mountain Actual Ct.	Mary Mountain Loss	Mary Mountain Est.	Total Actual Ct.	Total Loss	Total Est.
1940-41	536	212	560	217	1	230	56		137	809	213	927
42	513	200		256	2		100			869	202	
43	742	9		122	2		100			964	11	
44	352	405		222	1		173	1		747	407	
45	445			324			163			932		
46	348	200		233			210	38		791	238	
47	442	7					101[a]					
48	313A	237		307			340			960	237	
49	396			205			525A			1126		
50	230	228		311A			553A			1094	228	
51							640A					
52	143	243		251	5		582	2		976	250	
53												
54	158[b]	77	106	461			858	62		1477	139	1425
55								288			288	1350
56	207	24		392	118		659	231		1258	373	
57	145	60		88			310	212		543	273	
58								12			12	
59		18						26			44	800
60												800

Year	212			169			488			869		Total
61	212			169			488			869	148	975
62		148	135		190			650			370	819
63		8	163		238			418			6	821
64		6	187		274			400			392[c]	
65	85	87		115		38	188	200	267	388	54	366
66	66	2		100		1	76		51	226	3	
67	80	1	82	123	124	1	194	194	1	397	4	400
68	70	1	80	160		2	188	200	1	418		440

[a] Firehole only.
[b] Count made during reduction.
[c] Includes 38 natural mortality.
Actual counts exclude loss figures.
Counts are postreduction, precalf.
Losses are mostly reductions.
Counts before 1951-52 are ground unless marked with A. Beginning in 1951-52, all counts are aerial.
Changes have been made from previous tabulations (Skinner and Alcorn, 1942-51) according to more accurate information.

Appendix V

DATA ON FETAL SIZES COMPILED FROM TABULATION OF LATE JANUARY 1941 (SKINNER 1941).

Sex	No. Sampled	Size Range	% < 1 lb.	% 1-5 lb.	% 5-10 lb.	% 10-15 lb.	% 15-20 lb.	% > 20 lb.
Female	28	4 lb. 5 oz.–23 lb.	0	7	25	29	29	11
Male	46	6 oz.–23 lb.	7	7	33	22	26	7
Total Sample	74		4	7	30	24	27	8

Type of Site	Species			Location		
		F	HV	L[a]	P	UL[b]
	Cusick Bluegrass			X		
	Kentucky Bluegrass	X				
	Giant Wild-rye			X		
	Sweetgrass			X	X	
	Timothy			X		
	Tufted Hairgrass	X	X	X	X	
Moist upland sites	Grass species	X	X			X
	Bluegrass	X	X	X		X
	Giant Wild-rye			X		
	Idaho Fescue	X	X	X		X
	Meadow Barley		X			
	Mountain Brome	X	X	X		
	Columbia Needlegrass			X		
	Richardson Needlegrass			X		
	Timber Oatgrass			X		
	Timothy	X				
Drier upland sites	Sedge (*Carex xerantica*)			X	X	
	Smallwing Sedge	X				
	Grass species	X				X
	Bluegrass	X	X			X
	Canby Bluegrass			X		
	Cusick Bluegrass			X		
	Kentucky Bluegrass	X				
	Sandberg Bluegrass			X		
	Idaho Fescue	X	X	X	X	
	Junegrass	X	X	X		
	Needle-and-Thread			X		
	Needlegrass				X	X
	Columbia Needlegrass		X			
	Richardson Needlegrass		X			
	Tufted Hairgrass					X
	Wheatgrass	X				X
	Bluestem Wheatgrass			X		
	Bluebunch Wheatgrass			X		
	Slender Wheatgrass		X			
	Thickspike Wheatgrass		X			
Mountain herbland	Sedge (*Carex aperta*					X
	C. raynoldsii					X
	C. xerantica)					X
	Ovalhead Sedge					X
	Smallwing Sedge					X
	Slender Rush					X
	Wire Rush					X

				Location		
Type of Site	Species	F	HV	L[a]	P	UL[b]
	Bluegrass					X
	Alpine Bluegrass					X
	Canby Bluegrass					X
	Idaho Fescue					X
	Meadow Barley					X
	Mountain Brome					X
	Needlegrass					X
	Purple Onion Grass					X
	Timothy					X
	Alpine Timothy					X
	Slender Wheatgrass					X
	Tufted Hairgrass					X
Drier mountain sites	Long-styled Rush					X
	Bluegrass					X
	Idaho Fescue					X
	Junegrass					X
	Timber Oatgrass					X
Subalpine meadows	Sedge (*Carex nova*					X
	C. platylepsis					X
	C. raynoldsii)					X
	Hepburn Sedge					X
	Smallwing Sedge					X
	Bluegrass					X
	Alpine Bluegrass					X
	Timberline Bluegrass					X
	Idaho Fescue					X
	Meadow Barley					X
	Alpine Timothy					X
	Tufted Hairgrass					X

F = Firehole
HV = Hayden Valley
L = Lamar
P = Pelican
UL = Upper Lamar

[a]Data is more complete for Lamar.
[b]All wet sites are at higher elevations.

References

ALLEE, W. C., O. PARK, A. E. EMERSON, T. PARK, and K. P. SCHMIDT. 1949. *Principles of animal ecology*. W. B. Saunders Co., Philadelphia, Pa. 837 p.

ANON. 1909-11. *Reports. In:* File No. 21 & 22. Buffalo. Yell. Natl. Park Archives.

———. 1912-13. *Reports. In:* File No. 21 & 22. Buffalo. Yell. Natl. Park Archives.

BAILEY, VERNON. 1930. *Animal life of Yellowstone National Park*. Charles E. Thomas, Springfield, Ill. 241 p.

BAILEY, VIRGINIA L., and N.E. BAILEY. 1949. *Woody plants of the western national parks*. University Press, Notre Dame, Ind. 274 p.

BARLOW, J. W., and D. P. HEAP. 1872. *Report of a reconnaissance of the basin of the upper Yellowstone in 1871*. U. S. Gov't. Printing Office, Washington, D.C. 43 p.

BARMORE, WILLIAM J. 1968. *Bison and brucellosis in Yellowstone National Park: a problem analysis*. Yell. Natl. Park. Typed report. 73 p.

BERGSTROM, R. C. 1964. *Competition between elk and phytophagous insects for food in the Lamar Valley, Yellowstone National Park*. Ph.D. Thesis. Univ. of Wyoming, Laramie. 107 p.

BLACKMORE, WM. (LORD). 1872. *Diary-fourth visit to the United States*. (Transcription, Western Range Cattle Industry Study. State Museum, Denver, Colo.) Yell. Natl. Park Library. Photocopy.

BOONE and CROCKETT CLUB. 1964. *Records of North American big game*. Holt, Rinehart & Winston, New York. 398 p.

BOOTH, W. E. 1950. *Flora of Montana. Part I. Conifers and monocots*. The Research Foundation at Montana State College. Bozeman. 232 p.

BOOTH, W. E., and J. C. WRIGHT. 1959. *Flora of Montana. Part II. Dicotyledons*. 1966. The Research Foundation at Montana State Univ., Bozeman. 305 p.

BOZEMAN AVANT-COURIER. 1883. *Game features of the Yellowstone Park*. 11 January.

———. 1883. *Park pencillings*. 22 February.

BURGER, JOHN F. 1967a. *Diptera: Rhagionidae. Effect of abundance on wildlife*. Rept. to the Natl. Park Serv. Yell. Natl. Park Library. Typed. 2 p.

———. 1967b. *Letter to Sup't. McLaughlin*, Yell. Natl. Park, 13 March 1967. Yell. Natl. Park Library. Typed. 4 p.

BURGESS, F. 1898-99. *Scout diary*. Yell. Natl. Park Archives.

CAHALANE, VICTOR H. 1944. Restoration of wild bison. *Trans. N. Am. Wildl. Conf.* **9**:135-143.

CHOQUETTE, LAURENT P. E., J. GUY COUSINEAU, and ERIC BROUGHTON. 1966. *Pathology*. Can. Wildl. Ser. Annual Report. p. 75-80.

CHRISTMAN, GENE N. 1971. The mountain bison. *The American West*. **8(3)**:44-47.

COLE, GLEN. 1969. *The elk of Grand Teton and southern Yellowstone National Parks*. Research Report GRTE—N-1. Mimeo. 192 p.

CONNER, A. H., and ROBERT CORNELL. 1958. Brucellosis in bison, elk, and moose in Elk Island National Park, Alberta, Canada. *Can. J. Comp. Med., Vet. Sci.* **22**:9-20.

COOK, CHARLES W., DAVID E. FOLSOM, and WILLIAM PETERSON. 1869. An exploration of the headwaters of the Yellowstone River in the year 1869. *In:* Haines, Aubrey ed. 1965. *The valley of the upper Yellowstone*. University of Oklahoma Press, Norman.

DELACY, WALTER W. 1876. A trip up the south Snake River in 1863, p. 113-143. *In: Contributions to the Historical Society of Montana*. V. I. Rocky Mountain Publishing Co., Helena.

DOANE, G. C. 1875. The report of Lieut. Gustavus C. Doane upon the so-called Yellowstone Expedition of 1870 to the Secretary of War. Appendix M. *In:* Cramton, Louis C. 1932. *Early history of Yellowstone National Park and its relation to national park policies.* U. S. Gov't Printing Office, Washington, D.C.

———. 1876. *Expedition of 1876-1877.* Yell. Natl. Park Library. Typed. 44 p.

DUNRAVEN, EARL OF. 1876. *The great divide.* Chatto & Windus, London, England. 382 p.

ETKIN, WILLIAM. 1964. Types of social organization in birds and mammals, p. 256-297. *In:* Etkin, William, ed. 1964. *Social behavior and organization among vertebrates.* University of Chicago Press. Chicago, Ill.

FRICK, E. J. 1951. Parasitism in bison. *J. Am. Vet. Med. Assoc.* **119**:386-387.

FRYXELL, FRITIOF M. 1926. A new high altitude limit for the American bison. *J. Mammal.* **7**:102-109.

FULLER, W. A. 1959. The horns and teeth as indicators of age in bison. *J. Wildl. Manage.* **23**:342-344.

———. 1960. Behavior and social organization of the wild bison of Wood Buffalo National Park, Canada. *Arctic.* **13**: 3-19.

———. 1961. The ecology and management of the American bison. *Extrait de la Terre et la Vie.* **2-1961**:286-304.

———. 1962. The biology and management of the Bison of Wood Buffalo National Park. *Can. Wildl. Serv. Wildl. Manage. Bull. Ser. 1, No. 16.* 52 p.

GARRETSON, MARTIN S. 1938. *The American bison.* New York Zool. Soc. 254 p.

GILMAN, N. L., and JOHN L. MCAULIFF. 1956. Brucellosis, p. 538-556. *In:* Fincher, M. G., ed. 1956. *Diseases of cattle.* American Veterinary Publishers, Inc., Evanston, Ill.

GRIMM, RUDOLF L. 1939. Northern Yellowstone winter range studies. *J. Wildl. Manage.* **3**:295-306.

GRINNELL, GEO. BIRD. 1876. Zoological report, p. 66-89. *In:* Ludlow, William. 1876. *Report on a reconnaissance from Carroll, Montana Territory, on the Up-* per Missouri, to the Yellowstone National Park. U. S. Gov't. Printing Office, Washington, D. C.

HAGUE, ARNOLD. 1893. The Yellowstone Park as a game reservation, p. 240-270. *In: American big game hunting, the book of the Boone & Crockett Club.* Forest & Stream Publishing Co., New York.

———. 1899. *Geology of Yellowstone National Park.* U. S. Geo. Survey. Monograph 32, Part 2. U. S. Gov't. Printing Office, Washington, D.C. 893 p.

HAINES, AUBREY, ed. 1955. *Osborne Russell's journal of a trapper.* Oregon Historical Society, Portland. 179 p.

———. 1963. History of Yellowstone National Park, p. 84-136. *In: A manual of general information on Yellowstone National Park.* Yell. Natl. Park. Mimeo.

HALLORAN, A. F. 1968. Bison (Bovidae) productivity on the Wichita Mountains Wildlife Refuge, Oklahoma. *Southwest Nat.* **13**:23-26.

HENDERSON, A. BART. 1870. *Narrative of a prospecting expedition to the East Fork and Clark's Fork of Yellowstone...1870.* (Original in Coe Collection, Yale Univ. Library.) Yell. Natl. Park Library. Typed transcript.

HOFER, T. E. 1927. *Letter to LeRoy Hill.* 5 February. Yell. Natl. Park Archives.

HOLMES, W. H. 1878. *Exploration of the Yellowstone National Park by the U. S. Geological and Geographical Survey of the Territories, 1878.* Yell. Natl. Park Library. Typed transcript. 43 p.

HOLT, PETER. 1899-1901. *Scout diary.* Yell. Natl. Park Archives.

HOUGH, EMERSON. 1894. *Forest and Stream's Yellowstone Park expedition of 1894.* Yell. Natl. Park Library. Newspaper account.

HOUSTON, DOUGLAS B. 1968. *The Shiras moose in Jackson Hole, Wyoming.* Grand Teton Natural History Assoc. Grand Teton Natl. Park. 110 p.

JONES, WILLIAM A. 1875. *Report upon the reconnaissance of Northwestern Wyoming including Yellowstone National Park, made in the summer of 1873.* U. S.

Gov't. Printing Office, Washington, D.C. 331 p.

KITTAMS, WALTER H. 1947-58. *Northern winter range studies.* 2 Vol. Yell. Natl. Park Library. Typed.

———. 1949. *Preliminary report on Hayden Valley bison range.* Yell. Natl. Park Library. Typed. 8 p.

LAKE STATION. 1898-1911. *Station record.* Yell. Natl. Park Archives.

———. 1911-18. *Station record.* Yell. Natl. Park Archives.

LE HARDY, PAUL. 1873. *Autobiography of Paul Le Hardy,* p. 95-104. (Typescript copied from handwritten 247 p. autobiography.) Yell. Natl. Park Library.

LIVINGSTON ENTERPRISE. 1885. *News article.* Mar. **7**:3; Dec. **12**:1; Dec. **19**:3.

LOCKER, BETTY. 1953. Parasites of bison in northwestern U.S.A. J. Parasitol. **39**:396-397.

MACARTHUR, ROBERT, and JOSEPH CONNELL. 1966. *The biology of populations.* John Wiley & Sons, New York. 200 p.

MCHUGH, TOM. 1958. Social behavior of the American Buffalo (*Bison bison bison*). *Zoologica.* 43, Part 1. 31 March 1958. 40 p.

MCDOUGALL. W. B., and HERMA A. BAGGLEY. 1956. *Plants of Yellowstone National Park.* Yell. Library and Museum Assoc. Yell. Natl. Park, Wyo. 186 p.

MARBLE, CHARLES. 1932. *Fifty years in and around Yellowstone National Park and miscellaneous notes.* Yell. Natl. Park Library. Typed. 36 p.

MEAGHER, M. 1966. *Lungworm* (Dictyocaulus *sp.*) *in bison of Yellowstone National Park.* Yell. Natl. Park Library. Typed. 8 p.

MECH, L. DAVID. 1966. *The wolves of Isle Royale.* Fauna of the Natl. Parks of the U.S. U.S. Gov't Printing Office, Washington, D.C. 210 p.

MORRISON, JAMES. 1897-98. *Scout diaries.* 2 Vol. Yell. Natl. Park Archives.

MURRI, ERNEST. 1968. *Interview of 5 May 1968 by Natl. Park Service personnel.* Yell. Natl. Park Archives. Tape recording.

NOWLIN, D. C. 1912. *Report on wild buffalo and elk, Yellowstone Park.* July 22-30. Typed. 5 p. *In:* File No. 21 & 22. Buffalo. 1909-11 inc. Yell. Natl. Park Archives.

OLDEMEYER, JOHN L. 1966. *Winter ecology of bighorn sheep in Yellowstone National Park.* M. S. Thesis. Colorado State Univ., Fort Collins. 107 p.

PARK, ED. 1969. *The world of the bison.* J. B. Lippincott Co., Philadelphia. Pa. 161 p.

PATTEN, D. T. 1963. Vegetational pattern in relation to environments in the Madison Range, Montana. *Ecol. Monogr.* **33**:375-406.

PATTIE, DONALD L., and NICOLAAS A. M. VERBEEK. 1967. Alpine mammals of the Beartooth Mountains. *Northwest Sci.* **41**:110-117.

PIERREPONT, EDWARD, 1884. *Fifth avenue to Alaska.* G. P. Putnam Sons, New York, 329 p.

POTTER, MRS. LENA. 1962. *Notes from an interview.* Yell. Natl. Park Archives. Tape recording.

QUORTRUP, ERLING R. 1945. *A report on brucellosis investigations, Yellowstone National Park.* Dec. 1-20, 1944. Yell. Natl. Park Library. Mimeo. 27 p.

RAYMOND, ROSSITER W. 1880. *Camp and cabin: sketches of life and travel in the west.* Fords, Howard & Hulbert, New York. 242 p.

RAYNOLDS, W. F. 1867. *Report of Brevet Colonel W. F. Raynolds, U. S. A., Corps of Engineers, on the exploration of the Yellowstone and Missouri Rivers in 1859-1860.* 40th Congr., 1st Sess. Senate Ex. Doc. No. 77. U. S. Gov't. Printing Office, Washington, D. C. 174 p.

ROBINETTE. W. LESLIE, JAY S. GASHWILER, DALE A. JONES, and HAROLD S. CRANE. 1955. Fertility of mule deer in Utah. *J. Wildl. Manage.* **19**:115-136.

ROE, FRANK GILBERT. 1951. *The North American buffalo.* University of Toronto Press, Canada. 957 p.

RUSH, W. M. 1932a. Bang's disease in Yellowstone National Park buffalo and elk herds. *J. Mammal.* **13**:371-372.

———. 1932b. *Northern Yellowstone elk study.* Mont. Fish Game Comm., Helena. 131 p.

SCOUTS. 1908-14. *Monthly reports.* Yell. Natl. Park Archives.

SKINNER, CURTIS K. 1941. *Special report on Yellowstone National Park bison.* Yell.

Natl. Park Bio. Files. 715-03. Buffalo (General). Typed.

SKINNER, CURTIS K., and WAYNE B. ALCORN. 1942-51. *History of the bison in Yellowstone Park.* Yell. Natl. Park Library. Typed report.

SKINNER, MORRIS F. 1965. *Letter to Dr. J. D. Love, U.S.G.S.* 19 Nov. Yell. Natl. Park Museum Files.

SKINNER, MORRIS F., and OVE C. KAISEN. 1947. The fossil *Bison* of Alaska and preliminary revision of the genus. *Bull. Am. Mus. Nat. His.* **89:** 127-256.

SNAKE RIVER STATION. 1897. *Monthly report, August.* Yell. Natl. Park Archives.

SODA BUTTE STATION. 1898. *Station record.* Yell. Natl. Park Archives.

SOIL CONSERVATION SERVICE. 1963. *Site condition survey, northern Yellowstone.* Yell. Natl. Park Bio. Files.

———. 1964. *Site condition survey, Hayden-Pelican Creek.* Yell. Natl. Park Bio. Files.

STEVENSON,DONALD. 1915-16. *Scout diary.* Yell. Natl. Park Archives.

SUPERINTENDENTS of the Yellowstone National Park. 1877-1915. *Annual reports.* Yell. Natl. Park Library.

———. 1903-21. *Journal.* Yell. Natl. Park Archives.

THUMB STATION. 1898-1916. *Station record.* Yell. Natl. Park Archives.

TIMMONS, WILLIAM. 1962. *Twilight on the range.* University of Texas Press, Austin. 223 p.

TUNNICLIFF, E. A., and H. MARSH 1935. Bang's disease in bison and elk in the Yellowstone National Park and on the National Bison Range. *J. Am. Vet. Med. Assoc.* **86:**745-752.

U. S. DEP. AGRIC. SOIL CONSERV. SERV. 1919-67. *Summary of snow survey measurements.* Wyoming, Casper. 152 p.

U.S. DEP. COMMER. WEATHER BUREAU. 1930-59. *Climatological summary for Yellowstone National Park.* Climatography of the U.S. No. 20-48. 2 p.

WHITTAKER, GEORGE. 1897-99. *Scout diaries.* 4 Vol. Yell. Natl. Park Archives.

WOOLF, ALAN. 1968. *Summer ecology of bighorn sheep in Yellowstone National Park.* M. S. Thesis. Colorado State Univ., Fort Collins. 112 p.

YOUNT, HARRY. 1880. Report of gamekeeper, p. 50. In: *Superintendents of the Yellowstone National Park. 1880.* Annual report. Yell. Natl. Park Library.

———. 1881. Report of gamekeeper, p. 62-63. In: *Superintendents of the Yellowstone National Park. 1881.* Annual report. Yell. Natl. Park Library.

Index

U. S. Department of the Interior

National Park Service

U. S. GOVERNMENT PRINTING OFFICE : 1973 O - 521-650